"This resource book will prove invaluable for those whose mission challenges them to cope with the long-term effects of stressful situations."
-Bruce Lackie, Ph.D.

"This book fills a significant gap in the trauma field by focusing on the impact of trauma experiences of missionaries and clergy, post traumatic stress and the intersection with scripture. It provides,for all of us, compelling insights into distinctive trauma-related aspects of missionaries and those involved in missionary and spiritually-related work – and does so with a refreshing clarity (alt: down-to-earth clarity). Because trauma inevitably arouses powerful beliefs and issues regarding God and a higher power, this book is of relevance to anyone working with and/or impacted by trauma."

-Dr. Ray Scurfield, Professor of Social Work
(University of Southern Mississippi), former Director of
the National Center for PTSD in Honolulu, and a Vietnam veteran

RECOVERING FROM
TRAUMATIC STRESS

A Guide for Missionaries

Stephanie Laite Lanham and Joyce Hartwell Pelletier

WILLIAM CAREY
LIBRARY

Published by William Carey Library
1605 E. Elizabeth Street
Pasadena, CA 91104 | www.missionbooks.org

Rosemary Lee-Norman, copyeditor
Amanda Valloza, graphic design

William Carey Library is a ministry of the
U.S. Center for World Mission
Pasadena, CA | www.uscwm.org

Printed in the United States of America

14 13 12 11 10   5 4 3 2 1 B P
2010800BP

Library of Congress Cataloging-in-Publication Data

Lanham, Stephanie Laite.
 Recovering from traumatic stress : a guide for missionaries / by Stephanie Laite Lanham And Joyce Pelletier.
   p. cm.
 Includes bibliographical references.
  ISBN 978-0-87808-020-5
  1. Psychic trauma. 2. Post-traumatic stress disorder. 3. Missionaries--Mental health.
 I. Pelletier, Joyce. II. William Carey Library. III. Title.
  RC552.T7L36 2010
  616.85'21--dc22
                            2010006307

To our husbands and families for supporting our mission efforts with prayer, finances, legal efforts (Sam), hard work, and long hours. We are blessed and thankful women!

In Memoriam

Gifford Hartwell, center of picture,
with technicians from HCJB-TV, the Voice of the Andes.

Gifford Newton Hartwell, missionary in Quito, Ecuador, from 1959-1967.
Gifford built the first television station for the country of Ecuador through generous contributions from General Electric (GE), and supportive members of the North Syracuse Baptist Church in North Syracuse, New York.

In the 1950's Gifford received word that a Christian short-wave radio station wanted to transition into television ministry. An engineer working at GE, Gifford began collecting scrap television equipment and was able to build a TV station in his garage over a period of two years. In 1958, Gifford sold the TV station to HCJB World Radio for a legal transaction of just $1.00. His friends at North Syracuse Baptist Church helped him crate and ship the TV station equipment to Quito, where the initial setup began while Gifford went to Costa Rica to learn Spanish. Gifford Hartwell's intention was to serve his Lord and the Ecuadorian people by providing Christian programming that would benefit the nation culturally, educationally, and spiritually.

In 1959 Gifford and other HCJB engineers introduced television to the nation of Ecuador at the annual country fair. Most of the Ecuadorians had never seen a television set and were amazed to see their images appear on closed-circuit TV.

During Gifford's two terms in Quito, television spread throughout the capital city.

Gifford taught technical TV courses to the radio technicians of Ecuador assisting in the transition to television. Certificates given to Gifford by the Radio Associations of Pichincha and Guayaquil read:

Honorable Mention to Gifford Hartwell
in recognition of your enthusiastic and strong efforts
to benefit the members of this society
by teaching intensive courses in television technology.
June 1964
November 1966

Gifford struggled with symptoms of stress-related anxiety throughout his lifetime. It is in memory of Gifford and other missionaries who have coped with trauma and stress that this book is written.

-Joyce Hartwell Pelletier, missionary daughter

Requiescat

The Armor of God

God's armor is protective and helps to defend us against all evil circumstances that may come our way. It is common for missionaries to experience traumatic events and attacks that may limit the effectiveness of their ministries. Don't be surprised if your spiritual struggles include emotional and psychological trauma. The armor of God is your defense and shield against the schemes of the evil one. Wear it. Polish it with scripture reading. Understand what the scripture means and you will grow in grace.

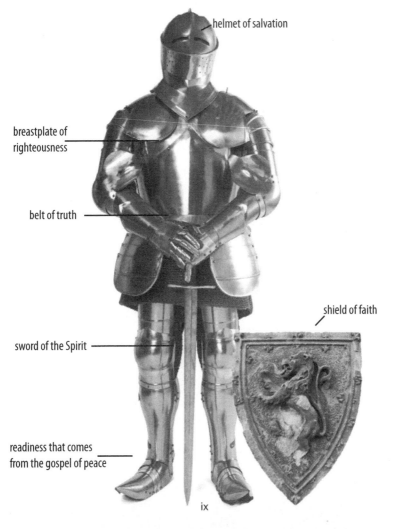

helmet of salvation

breastplate of righteousness

belt of truth

shield of faith

sword of the Spirit

readiness that comes from the gospel of peace

Be strong in the Lord and in his mighty power. Put on the full armor of God so that you can take your stand against the devil's evil schemes. For our struggle is not against flesh and blood, but against the rulers, against the authorities, against the powers of this dark world and against the spiritual forces of evil in the heavenly realms. Therefore put on the full armor of God so that when the day of evil comes, you may be able to stand your ground, and after you have done everything, to stand.

Stand firm then, with the belt of truth buckled around your waist, with the breastplate of righteousness in place, and with your feet fitted with the readiness that comes from the gospel of peace. In addition to this, take up the shield of faith, with which you can extinguish the flaming arrows of the evil one. Take the helmet of salvation and the sword of the Spirit, which is the word of God. And pray in the spirit on all occasions, with all kinds of prayers and requests. With this in mind, be alert and always keep on praying for the saints.
-Eph 6:10-18

The Armor of PTSD

PTSD can build armor around a missionary as well, but it is a self-defeating armor. Unlike the armor of God which strengthens and protects, traumatic armor numbs the senses, reduces concentration, invades memories, and disturbs sleep. The armor of PTSD restricts a missionary from authentic relationships, sensitivity to the needs of others, and a normal range of feelings. A person armored with PTSD often does not even realize the armor is there. Truth and peace are squelched.

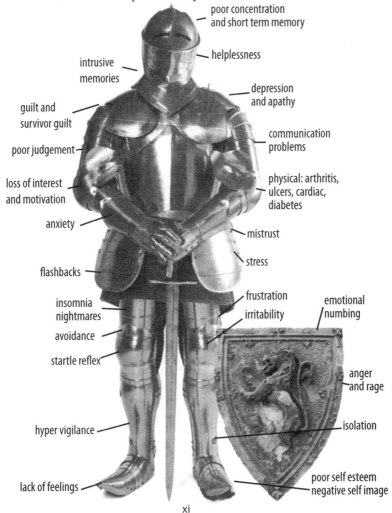

poor concentration
and short term memory

intrusive memories

helplessness

guilt and survivor guilt

depression and apathy

poor judgement

communication problems

loss of interest and motivation

physical: arthritis, ulcers, cardiac, diabetes

anxiety

mistrust

flashbacks

stress

insomnia nightmares

frustration
irritability

emotional numbing

avoidance

startle reflex

anger and rage

hyper vigilance

isolation

lack of feelings

poor self esteem
negative self image

Contents

Preface

The signs and symptoms of traumatic stress, or symptoms meeting the full diagnostic criteria for Post-Traumatic Stress Disorder (PTSD), can be debilitating. Missionaries may have experienced violent and disturbing situations while working throughout the world. Post-trauma symptoms may be expressed as an emotional response resulting from experiencing trauma. PTSD is a normal reaction to an abnormal event.

If you, or the missionary in your life, have experienced one or perhaps more of the signs or symptoms described within these pages, one of you may have a diagnosis of PTSD or another related diagnosis.

There is help; you are never alone. Our Lord knows your struggles and will direct you to those who can help. Help may be found within the Body of Christ; God may direct you to a skilled professional who is the best to supply your care. The key is to receive the best care for your heart and soul—only then will the spiritual, emotional, and physical healing take hold (Exod. 15:26, 23:25, Matt. 12:15, 14:35-36).

Within these pages you will find the information and resources to support you as you look for healing. The resources will lead you and your family to comfort and healing, and might also help you reconnect with old friends or make some new ones. You can regain peace of mind, or maybe find peace for the first time.

Two long-time friends created this book for you. Together, the authors have experienced nearly 60 years of married life, raised six kids, and lived through lots of laughter, tears, and *trauma*. They share a dedication to Jesus Christ.

Stephanie Laite Lanham, adult psychiatric mental health nurse practitioner and co-author of this book, first wrote *Veterans and Families' Guide to Recovering from PTSD* for the veteran community at large. That booklet was so well received, with nearly 600,000 copies in print thus far, that the Military Order of the Purple Heart National Service Organization

(MOPH) supported the expanded version for nationwide distribution through its fourth edition published during the spring of 2007.

Joyce Pelletier, licensed clinical professional counselor, co-author of this book and former missionaries' kid in Ecuador, read the original book and immediately saw the similarities between Veterans' experiences and those of missionaries. Joyce and Stephanie decided the book needed to be rewritten for missionaries, third culture kids, and all who support missionary families with their prayers and finances. This publication is the result.

This book will teach you about the symptoms of post-trauma and how to recognize them in your life. It will begin to strengthen you, and teach you how to talk to your family members and others about your experiences. It is our hope that through understanding you may begin, with God's help, to regain a sense of peace.

We have included writing samples generously shared from the hearts of missionaries and families who may have walked in your shoes, as well as resources that will be helpful in your healing process.

A chapter has been added about Secondary Traumatic Stress. Although not yet recognized in the Diagnostic and Statistical Manual of Mental Disorders (DSM-IV), there are many spouses, children, peers, and significant others who may recognize these symptoms. We hope these insights will bring you one step closer to seeking support.

There is help available for you and your family. Stephanie and Joyce have looked to the Christian community for resources and also to worldwide resources from which you may benefit.

Many missions' organizations have trained counselors within their networks who can assist you with counseling as well as member and respite care. If you are concerned about confidentiality, there are Christian practitioners throughout the world who will work with you without disclosing any private information to others. Some counselors are willing to email you on the field and assist you in any way possible. In the back of this book we have listed some valuable references and resources.

Welcome to a book born of love in Christ, belief in missions' work, faith that missionaries and their families can teach one another with their gifts of writing, and assurance that our powerful God can heal....always.

Moving forward together,
Stephanie and Joyce

Acknowledgments

We applaud all who serve through missionary work in the past, present, and future. This book is for you to share with your family, friends, doctors, nurses, pastors, sponsoring churches, and anyone else that might need information and assistance.

Abiding thanks to all missionaries who have offered their inspirational support throughout our world, and who continue to do so, often at great personal risk.

To those who contributed soul-baring writings to this endeavor to reach out to fellow missionaries and those who care about them, thank you. Your efforts are appreciated and will bring healing to suffering souls.

Thank you to those who serve on the Board of Directors of Solomon PTSD Recovery Project. We will do great works for many. Thank you for not closing your eyes to this opportunity. We will not be asleep in the light.

Thank you to Sunrise Seminars counselors for going out into communities with inspiring messages of hope, renewal, positive parenting, bettering marriages, improving emotional health and many other topics about "Life is good—Live it Christian!"

Stephanie, Joyce, and those working on this project, are continually appreciative to the many missionaries who contributed heartfelt writings to this book.

Abbreviations

AA .... Alcoholics Anonymous
ADHD .... Attention Deficit Hyperactivity Disorder
BC .... Board Certified
DSM-IV .... Diagnostic and Statistical Manual of Mental Disorders
ERP .... exposure and relapse prevention
GE .... General Electric
HCJB .... Heralding Christ Jesus' Blessings Global Radio Station
LCPC .... Licensed Clinical Professional Counselor
LPC .... Licensed Professional Counselor
MA .... Masters of the Arts
MED .... Masters in Education
MDiv .... Masters in Divinity
MFT .... Marriage and Family Therapy
MK .... Missionary Kid
MOPH .... Military Order of the Purple Heart National Service Organization
NA .... Narcotics Anonymous
OA .... Overeaters Anonymous
OCD .... Obsessive Compulsive Disorder
PMH-NP .... Psychiatric Mental Health-Nurse Practitioner
PTS .... Patients
PTSD .... Post-Traumatic Stress Disorder
RNC .... Registered Nurse Certified
SI .... Suicidal Ideation
STSD .... Secondary Traumatic Stress Disorder

Symptoms

of

Trauma

Not Whole
By Stephanie Laite Lanham, 2004

When I was tiny I wondered why you looked away when I talked to you or
sometimes stopped reading in the middle of a story
You got angry so quickly and I did not know why.
I thought I had made you mad.
I knew you were angry at somebody, everybody.
Something.
Someone had hurt you.
Something had hurt you.
You were always looking for someone.
Something was missing.
You were lost.
No one could find you even when you were in the room.
I thought I was in the way sometimes.
There was nothing I could do to help and sometimes I think I made it
worse.
I could not get close to you.
I started to punish myself in ways you punished yourself.

Our family was not whole.
Nighttime was alive with footsteps and tears.
Love was in our home.
Battlefields were in your head.
The flag flew in our hearts, above our door,
And reminded you of love lost.
What we did not know how to give
What we could not understand.
What we could not know.

Now I look away as I read to my little one.
I sometimes cannot sleep at night.
Anger threatens to overwhelm me.
I am alone.
I cannot feel as I am told I should.
Your battlefields have made their way into my head.

Anger

Jeff came to South America to do the Lord's work, but his short fuse continued to get him into trouble with the natives. "Muy bravo," the national workers would say, meaning he had quite a temper and was unpredictable. Over time, the nationals learned to keep their distance and the missions board began to look for ways to isolate him. Although his technical work was valuable, his personal relationships suffered greatly.

What is anger?

Anger is a powerful emotion that people experience for many reasons. Anger may be expressed with physical and emotional agitation, frustration, indignation, exasperation, hostility, or extreme displeasure. Anger can be expressed both physically and emotionally towards self or others. Anger may be used as a distraction from sadness and helplessness. Sometimes couples fight to avoid feelings of anger and sadness.

Aggression may surface as a result of the anger, causing one to engage in destructive behavior toward self, others, or property. Aggression may manifest in verbal attacks, violent behavior, general hostility, agitation, or threats toward self and others. Anger is a powerful emotion that can take control in the strongest of individuals and seems to have a life of its own.

People experience anger in varied degrees from mild annoyance to extreme rage. When people express anger appropriately, the outcome can be positive, promoting growth and facilitating change. When expressed in a negative or dangerous way, the results may include hurt feelings to self, family, or friends with physical or emotional injury. Depression can be a form of anger turned inward.

Some missionaries are unaware of their feelings of anger. Believing their anger is sinful, they become more comfortable with feelings of sadness. Anger is a natural God-given emotion that can energize and protect during times of danger. The anger itself is not sinful, but behavior inspired by anger may cause hurt.

It is better to express angry feelings in a safe way than to keep them inside. Eventually the feelings will rise to the surface and the volcano will blow. It is better to talk with those who understand, those who have been there, and those who have walked where you have walked, rather than to keep angry feelings inside where they can make you sick.

What can I do to control my anger?

There is safety and understanding in sharing your anger. It may seem impossible, but you can learn to redirect angry feelings. Anger management therapy is a positive choice and an important one. Managing angry feelings when they occur in a way that is supported by scripture is important: "In your anger, do not sin." (Eph. 4:26)

Anger may affect your ministry as well as relationships at work, within the family, and around you. When anger is suppressed or not expressed in a healthy way, those around you may recognize a change in your body language, tone of voice, or actions. It is important to let someone, such as a counselor, friend, or family member give you feedback about what they see. Feedback is not easy to hear or give but it can make a difference by opening a door for communication.

When anger surfaces unexpectedly, it is important to pause to think before you act. Anger may lead to impulsivity, causing one to say or do something that is later regretted. "A fool gives full vent to his anger, but a wise man keeps himself under control." (Prov. 29:11) It is important to walk away, calm down, and think about possible consequences.

Learn the specific triggers to your anger. What leads to or "triggers" your angry outbursts? It is usually not about the thing, event, or person at whom you are directing your anger at that moment. This awareness can be enlightening and lead to healing.

Learn to do something distracting instead of attacking. Use empathy to understand why someone seems to be confronting you. Develop healthy coping skills to use right away when you sense angry feelings stirring. Take positive action by going on a walk, engaging in a sport you love, giving yourself time out, praying, talking to a support person, writing in a journal, or drawing what you are feeling. Keep a verse about God's love and peace nearby where you can read it in times of anger. Imagine yourself as calm, see yourself making positive, healthy choices—then make them. Develop a safety plan to have ready whenever you suddenly experience a trigger that could lead to an angry outburst. Learn your personal triggers to anger and then avoid them whenever possible.

You will need to practice these skills, and in time, your fuse will lengthen. With God's help, you will be able to manage your anger so you are more comfortable and at peace with yourself.

Anxiety/hyperarousal

My husband was driving our car in Africa with my daughter and me aboard. Tragically, we struck a young Muslim man and killed him. We took the body to the hospital and then went to the police station. I was frightened when my husband went back to the scene of the accident with a scary-looking official, while I was left behind at the station with my young daughter. I didn't know what would happen next, and I didn't know if we were safe in the middle of the police compound with no one around and an open gate. Since then, I've been afraid whenever we drive anywhere.

What is anxiety?

Anxiety (root word—"angst") is the body's normal alarm system alerting us to danger. Anxiety provides energy to get things done, move through the day productively, and to stay safe. Anxiety is a biological, emotional, and psychological response to a traumatic experience, and a normal response to an abnormal situation. It may get out of control, however, so a sense of dread creeps over you. This may lead to greater anxiety and excessive worries. Although scripture reminds one to "cast all your anxiety on him because he cares for you" (I Pet. 5:7), sometimes anxiety can be overwhelming, making it difficult to "cast your anxiety on him" even knowing well how much God cares for us. This may lead to a cycle of more anxiety as guilt creeps in, especially if the missionary is a respected leader who does not appear to suffer anxiety. How painful to suffer in silence...

Anxiety or hyperarousal of the senses can be a personal "alarm bell" that will not shut off. This inner alarm may grow like a beating drum getting louder inside your chest as you experience excessive worries or fears more intensely. General anxiety may not be related to the initial trigger. Anxiety may show itself as fear of not knowing what comes next, or dread about the future and not knowing how to make it change.

Symptoms of anxiety include muscle tension, trembling, shaking, shortness of breath, pounding heart, increased heart rate, dry mouth, dizziness, irritability, sleep disturbance, constricted pupils, and difficulty concentrating. Anxiety, if untreated, can lead to panic attacks especially if the missionary is exposed to something that reminds him of a prior traumatic event.

Panic attack symptoms are an expression of anxiety, but they are more intense and can mimic a heart attack. In addition, the symptoms may include feelings of choking, chills or hot flashes, numbness, tingling, or chest pain. A person may mention the word "panic" when describing how they feel.

Anxiety affects interpersonal relationships because the missionary may overreact to feeling a loss of control of the environment. There may be tunnel vision, anger, and isolation. Everyone surrounding the anxious individual may share in the experience of angst when symptoms increase.

What can I do about my anxiety?

Fortunately, anxiety is treatable! The key is to recognize anxious thoughts, and to learn how to bring your thoughts captive to the power of Christ (2 Cor. 10:5) so anxiety does not take over your life. Anxiety is difficult to overcome, but not impossible with God's help, education, and the best treatment for you.

Learn to identify the triggers to your anxiety as a key to regaining control. Most importantly, give yourself and loved ones the opportunity to get support. Talking with a counselor can be the first positive step for anyone experiencing feelings of anxiety. It is important to learn about the biological changes that take place during anxious times, and relaxation skills for countering your symptoms. With education, treatment, and possibly prescription medication there is hope for recovery to a "new normal" where you will regain composure and peace.

Healthy life skills are important for reducing anxiety. They include exercising regularly to get and stay healthy, eating properly, allowing for family time, taking down times, and scheduling periods of solitude, meditation, and prayer. Coping skills that help with anxiety are listening to calming music, sitting in a comfortable place with eyes closed, focusing on slow regular breathing, visualizing scenes of heaven with thoughts of God's love, and finding a relaxing hobby. Restructuring your day so tension is reduced helps to lower your anxiety; you will be amazed at how small changes make a big difference! It is also helpful to develop a written safety plan to have with you when anxiety is triggered. Eventually you will not feel the symptoms as much as you do now. Give yourself time; for time, as we have said, is a great healer.

Chronic Pain

As a child I was sexually assaulted on the mission field and also witnessed the death of a close family member. Throughout my lifetime, I've had a host of medical issues. Doctors are not sure what causes the pain I experience in my joints. Some think I have arthritis or fibromyalgia. My pain seems to come and go in intensity, but I am never completely pain-free. Some days I function quite well, and some days I can barely walk.

What is chronic pain?

Chronic pain is pain that lasts longer than six months. Sometimes the cause is unknown. Chronic pain is frustrating and can lead to depression, low self-esteem and feelings of anger. Pain interferes with daily activity and relationships when the missionary becomes moody or irritable. Life can be disrupted by chronic pain. Response to pain varies among each person depending on the location of the injury, the cause, one's pain threshold, personality, or co-morbid stressors. Not all pain is due to injury. The meaning of illness or disability, according to the missionary's culture and benefits received, will also play a part in adjustment to and acceptance of chronic pain.

Physical symptoms secondary to chronic pain can include increase in blood pressure, pulse, and respirations. Non-verbal body language such as facial grimace, moaning, or guarded posturing may indicate pain in an uncomplaining, but suffering missions worker. It is essential to establish treatment on several fronts.

You need to find the source of your pain and be treated medically. Emotional and spiritual needs are also essential to your wellbeing. You may need a pain specialist in addition to a counselor or whomever you chose to seek for information, and your primary care provider. Your provider will make referrals within your community. It is hard to be patient when you are in pain, but help is on the way.

What can I do to cope with my chronic pain?

Be sure you have seen medical professionals for good treatment so you know why you are experiencing pain. This may be difficult, depending on where you are serving. If you are told emotional pain is causing you physical pain, unconditional support will be helpful for you and your family.

Some forms of chronic pain may respond to exercise, such as walking, swimming, or biking. Be sure to get approval from your primary care provider before you begin any exercise program.

In some cases physical therapy, biofeedback, neurofeedback, abdominal breathing, visualization, guided imagery, meditation, acupuncture, or yoga are beneficial in helping you learn to relax so you can better control the pain. Each of these interventions has proven effective with chronic pain. You will have to see what can work for you. Adequate rest is sometimes a difficult goal, but a worthy one as fatigue makes fighting pain much more difficult. Using stress reduction techniques is important as it encourages relaxation. If the missionary can become more relaxed physically and emotionally, the pain level should decrease.

Prescription medication may be helpful for some to improve quality of life. Referrals to the best professionals who will help you medically and psychologically are essential with chronic pain. Remember that you are never alone. If you see one professional and you are not pleased, then ask to be referred to another.

Compulsions

The natives broke into our shed and stole our bicycles, which were our main source of transportation around town. The national worker stole some of our food and money. After that Jerry became obsessed with locking doors. He would go back to the same door several times to make sure he locked it. He checked our equipment over and over, checked and double-checked, until I was worried that he was losing his faith in God's ability to provide for us and keep us safe.

What are compulsions?

Thoughts or behaviors that are repeated in an effort to avoid fear and anxiety caused by obsessions may become compulsions. Becoming compulsive means repeating a thought or behavior until it begins to interfere with daily life. Compulsive behavior is specific according to rules and rituals set by the individual. Common compulsions include chronic hand washing, cleaning the same room or object repeatedly, grooming, or repeating a song or word. Ritual prayers can also become a compulsion. Some sufferers "check" objects, such as door locks, or appliances to be sure they are turned off, or drawers to be sure they are shut. Others turn lights on and off. Excessive shopping, collecting items, the need for constant approval, or making phone calls may become compulsions. Compulsions distract from anxiety, but hinder you from working on more important issues.

Order, frugality, and neatness are necessary for people to some degree. Orderliness can also become compulsive and "over-the-top". Some missionaries might say, "OCD (obsessive compulsive disorder) is okay for me, it keeps me organized." But when compulsions are strong, they may become a force that paralyzes everyday life even in a leader. You may experience compulsive eating, drinking, gambling, lying—even missions work can become compulsive.

Missionaries with compulsions may recognize on some level their behavior has begun to get out of control, or someone may try to make them aware of it, but compulsions are difficult to stop. Compulsions will begin to affect your family life and ministry. Relationships will suffer because compulsions take up time and become stronger than the desire to interact in a loving way with others. Seeking advice and help before compulsions become a way of life is wise, and a sign of character strength. More effective individuals will ask the Lord to help guide them to a healthy outcome, which will ultimately strengthen every area of their lives.

What can I do about my compulsions?

Like other symptoms of anxiety following trauma, compulsions may become more manageable with support, encouragement, prayer, and treatment including learning alternative behaviors with positive coping skills. A counselor can help you recover and be free from the pain of performing these rituals. You will learn why you do them and recognize triggers to the actions. With your counselor, you may work to gain clues as to how everyday behaviors became compulsions. In many cases repetitive behaviors have been going for a long time. You will learn positive coping skills and specific exercises with which to face obsessions, fears, or anxieties. Learning to rethink and behave differently takes time. Missionaries with a firm compulsion may have to work with their counselor to form a new way to do things. A counselor can assess your needs and make appropriate referrals for ongoing support. Prescription medication and ERP (exposure and relapse prevention) may be helpful, too. In time, with honesty, support, and behavior changes you will be free from the power of compulsions.

You are not alone. Many believers who have struggled with compulsions have been able to overcome with God's help and treatment. It can be a comfort to discover reasons why you are experiencing compulsions. Step out of the box and begin to heal. Don't be afraid to call someone for help.

Confusion

*After our sudden evacuation from the violence of political revolt, I felt
so exhausted and relieved to be safe, but the next morning I woke up in*

the USA and didn't know where I was. Everything was so drastically different! I couldn't remember what to do. I didn't know how to live. I felt like I had to touch things in the room to center myself and in order to make things seem real.

What is confusion?

Confusion is an uncomfortable feeling of inattentiveness, with thoughts seeming to come and go quickly, along with memory problems. While confusion is common immediately after a traumatic event, prolonged confusion can lead to feelings of frustration, disruptive behavior, difficulty performing daily living skills, and isolation from family and friends. The missionary may become unaware of time and place. Without a clear understanding of "here and now" the individual cannot focus well enough to communicate effectively.

Confusion may look like disorientation, decreased attention span, restlessness, anxiety, fear, confabulation, rambling speech, belligerence, combative behavior, depressed mood, or memory loss. The missionary's relationship with everyone is affected. If someone experiences confusion, then intervention and support are often required to insure safety.

What can I do to deal with confusion?

Coping with confusion can be difficult because you may *need* to let others help you. Missionaries are trained to take care of themselves. It is difficult enough to ask for help—but when confused asking for help is all the more difficult.

It is important to learn healthy, positive coping skills when you are not confused so if you experience a "trigger" and become confused you can safely respond. Getting connected with a support person, whether a fellow missionary, trusted family member, friend or professional is critical for success in coping with any emotional, medical, spiritual or psychiatric concern. Your support partner can help lead you to the best person to teach you positive coping skills to promote well-being.

Confusion often makes it difficult to sleep well at night. Good sleep hygiene is something you can learn. Sleep hygiene includes minimal caffeine, regular bed time hours—often difficult on the mission field—and gentle exercise until back in shape. Exercise is a good starter for regaining a clear state of mind. Relaxation skills, including specific prayer for peace of mind, are important also. Taking time for a deep breath will help you become calm when you feel anxious.

Keep a written safety plan close at hand at all times with names and numbers for times when you may not feel as "clear." This will increase your feeling of security if confusion occurs. You will learn to trust your safety plan and depend on it and on the people you may call in times of need. You will grow stronger as your confidence grows.

You will learn triggers to confusion, which may include haunting memories or an everyday sound. As you practice reality-grounding skills you will learn and your frustrations will decrease. Your quality of life will improve. Talking with someone who understands is very helpful. Safety is vital.

Medication is helpful in some cases. Ask your medication management provider what might work best for you. It is important that you feel your provider is listening and that your caregivers are able to work together on your behalf.

Crisis

Gunfire began echoing right next to the front wall of the missionary school campus and all along the east side. When the shooting started, we hurriedly rounded up everyone and flew into the main building, landing on the floor in record time. We all lay flat, facedown, hugging the cement walls for greater protection, in case any bullets should penetrate our building. The fighting raged on, loud and fierce. There had been talk of an evacuation since earlier the day before the shooting started, but it was still not safe to evacuate us. Sometimes the utter breadth and depth of emotions involved in all the many scenarios of events those last few days are almost too much to comprehend. Where does one go with all this? However does one begin to process and integrate all this stuff? I don't know. -Ruth

What is crisis?

Crisis is both an internal and external response that may occur following a stressful event which is perceived as a threat to the individual. Crisis may result from a seemingly small occurrence that becomes "the last straw" or an unexpected death. Living through a political revolt or war, life as a hostage, seclusion without the guarantee of safety, or a remote life having little contact with the familiar suggests a daily crisis of various magnitudes. You may have lived through "crises" if you are reading this booklet. Some crisis responses are more difficult to overcome than others. Your individual response to crisis is as unique as your personality. Your response is in part determined by your crisis preparation or lack thereof.

The body responds in many ways in a crisis. Your pulse may race because your heart is beating faster, your face may flush (get pink), and your head pound. You may have feelings of panic. Where you once managed dozens of workers with large projects, you are now in crisis over picking up the kids on time. What is this all about? You suddenly feel vulnerable, weak and out of control.

Counselors and mental health workers are uniquely qualified to help you debrief (talk) after a crisis. You will review how the crisis you have experienced as a missionary has affected you and your family. You will find there have been good and not-so-good feelings within the experience. Research shows that debriefing and "processing" or talking about your thoughts and feelings is helpful after having experienced a crisis, according to the International Critical Incident Stress Foundation. You may have wondered about God's protection as well as questioned his purpose concerning why you suffered. C.S Lewis has much to teach us in his work, *The Problem of Pain* as he wrestles with the question of a loving and merciful God and his suffering, faithful people.

When one has symptoms of post-traumatic stress, the threshold for crisis in that individual is lower. You need support and communication with people who understand.

What can I do to cope with crisis?

You can learn to spot triggers to anxiety that cause you to become susceptible to a crisis response. You can learn positive coping skills to use when triggers occur, such as rhythmic breathing and calling a specific support person. Once you have problem-solved, learned effective coping skills, and have seen the positive results, then you can better face any crisis.

There are counselors, pastoral counselors and many types of licensed counselors trained to work with those who have experienced trauma. These skilled professionals know how to teach missionaries and their families the necessary skills to cope with crisis so they can return to a *new normal*. You will regain a sense of hope, confidence in God, and renew your ability to live your life. You will once again be able to face a crisis without the fear you now hold within. You will learn to talk about how you respond to anxiety because of *triggers* from the past, and you will make a safety plan to use every day. An effective safety plan includes names and numbers of support people to call who will be there for you immediately should problems or crises arise. (See our section on Safety Plan).

If you ever have thoughts of wanting to hurt yourself or others, then *this is a crisis*. Please, do not wait; seek help immediately, the first time. Tell someone. Do not put off the opportunity to feel better.

Delusions

The doctor told George not to go to the Andes, because the high altitude could damage his already-weakened heart. Believing that God had called him, he went to the mission field anyway and found that his heart was fine during his two terms of service. Years later, George refused heart surgery because he believed that the doctors only wanted his money and were not telling him the truth about his failing heart. He stopped listening to doctors' advice, called them "quacks," and believed that they were out to get him. By the time George knew he was dying, it was too late to operate on his heart.

What are delusions?

Delusions are fixed beliefs one has about life, which are false, but have some basis in reality. Delusional thinking may lead to feelings of anxiety and paranoia because there is a loss of touch with reality. It is common for those experiencing delusions to deny they are experiencing them, or to behave in irrational ways that others do not understand. The missionary may feel confused and unsafe as delusions can be frightening.

Delusions may seem completely real. The missionary may believe he is re-experiencing trauma and fear. The family's response to someone experiencing delusions is often confusion and concern for their mental state, depending on the severity of the delusion and the coping supports in place. Education is important for the missionary and family so everyone will understand delusional thinking.

There are multiple causes for delusions, both medical and psychiatric. A correct diagnosis is important. You will need a primary care provider to rule out medical concerns, as is true with most of the symptoms described in this booklet. Whenever possible, your providers need to communicate with one another to provide you with the best bio-psycho-social, *collaborative* care.

Formulating a safety plan ahead of time is wise so everyone, including the missionary, knows what to do should a delusion occur. Names and numbers of support people, family, friends, health care providers and places are important to list on your safety plan. When you experience a trigger to a delusion, put the safety plan into action. With practice it will work for you.

What can I do to cope with delusions?

It is essential to learn to identify triggers to delusional thinking. You can learn to do this with education, support, and encouragement. Those who suffer from post-trauma may experience delusional thinking as well as the other symptoms listed and described in this booklet. The key is to learn to recognize the symptoms and their triggers, and to learn positive coping skills to better and more safely live with the symptoms. Some symptoms may vanish when you learn the new coping skills. Other symptoms may remain, but lessen, and be less intrusive to your improved quality of life.

With help you can learn to have control over your thoughts and have a disciplined prayer life, rebuilding trust in the Lord to help and guide you. Some missionaries will avoid delusions by using relaxation exercises, or by talking to someone if they begin to notice a change in their thoughts that is not reality-based, in order to reconnect with reality. Writing down thoughts, drawing or painting, art therapy, exercising, or beginning a hobby can be tools to refocus the mind back to what is real. It is important to avoid social isolation. Spending time with others who love and support you can boost your confidence and allow a connection with reality. Should faulty thoughts or delusions creep in, your supporters offer a check-in with the important safety plan you will use.

Denial

After the war, Bob felt completely dead to his emotions. He had lived through the worst of events, protecting himself by not allowing himself to feel the depths of his own fear, pain, or sorrow. His staff and coworkers told him he had been remarkably calm, and looked to Bob's stable leadership to guide their mission through the crisis. When Bob returned to the states, he spent the next few months traveling to raise money for the mission, and talking about the way God had carried them through the war. Bob believed he was "fine" and didn't need counseling. What Bob didn't realize was that everyone around him was having trouble connecting with him emotionally. He was unable to display empathy for others, and had closed off his heart from the compassionate heart of Christ.

What is denial?

Denial is the refusal to acknowledge the truth, either consciously or unconsciously. Denial is a defense mechanism used to protect against anxiety or emotional pain. It is a coping skill that can protect you from stress, but denial can also backfire and make you feel worse. It can restrict the positive emotions while pushing away negative emotions—for a while. Those who go through traumatic events may be using denial unconsciously to avoid dealing with painful memories and losses.

Missionaries may try to convince themselves that everything is fine and help is not needed. The truth may be that their lives are in chaos and they are having a difficult time functioning. Some missionaries have difficulty accepting reality because it may imply vulnerability or a lack of faith in God's protection. Others are concerned that if they tell the complete truth, their supporters will not continue to keep them on the field and their ministry will end. Missionary loyalties are deep, and the pressures to present the Lord's work in the best possible light are overwhelming leaving them feeling out of control and terrified so denial feels safer than reality.

Psalm 51:6 says, "You desire honesty from the heart, so you can teach me to be wise in my inmost being." God knows our innermost struggles and wants us to face the truth about our losses, mishaps, confusion, and fears. He will help us to do this gently and with support as we open our hearts to him. Healing might not feel gentle at times, but the result will be a kinder and gentler spirit and a farther-reaching ministry than ever you thought possible.

God is bigger than the difficulties of missions' life. He is able to restore life and resolve problems for those who talk honestly and seek help about their struggles on the field.

What can I do to avoid using denial as a defense mechanism?

Learning to discuss your feelings and emotions takes time for most people. For you to be able to talk honestly about your losses, you must first establish an environment of trust, support, encouragement and confidentiality. (This is yet another reason to seek a qualified, licensed professional). Building trust takes time. It can be hard to ask for help. Finding a confidential counselor or pastor is the first step in honest disclosure. Those who experience violence, death, or traumatic events often have difficulty expressing themselves. You will need *support* when learning to problem-solve bad habits that you have developed. In time you will discover the personal stressors which have triggered the use of denial as a defense mechanism.

Consider the possible negative outcome of not seeking help. The problems that are causing you to live in denial must be addressed for healing to start. Freedom from denial will allow honest communication to come into your life. As you gain insight and learn to problem solve effectively, your faith in God will grow. You will no longer need the defense mechanism of denial. You will live in truth, peace and…reality.

If the ministry in which you are working has not succeeded to the extent you had hoped and prayed, it does not mean you are a failure or that God is not pleased with your service. Working with your support person or professional therapist, you will learn to identify the fears, unrealistic threats, and feelings of grief, loss, and anxiety-provoking triggers to your denial. Once you have used newly-learned coping skills and have experienced positive outcomes, your confidence will be renewed.

Denial can magnify an existing problem. It is essential to develop the skills needed to face life's situations openly, honestly, and realistically. You can learn to walk in honesty and faith in the present moment, one day at a time, without the need to deny anything. Almighty God cares about you and supports you; you are able to talk to someone who understands anything is possible.

Dependence

Julie appeared confident and motivated, but after the assault she lost faith in herself and in God's ability to keep her safe. She seemed to always be looking for approval from others, going out of her way to avoid rejection. She developed migraine headaches, and began to choose friends with strong opinions who would tell her what to do.

What is dependence?
Dependence is relying too much on someone for constant support. Dependence can lead to an unhealthy need for physical contact, attention, help, approval, or repeated praise from others. Dependency problems can cause confusion and difficulty in life such as treatment resistance, which is common. Missionaries or missionary kids (MKs) may be overly dependent, resist caring for themselves, feel helpless, cling to others, express somatic complaints, demand extreme care, and become angry easily. Third-culture kids may become used to others caring for them and come to expect it.

While it is normal for missionaries who have experienced a traumatic event to need extra care for a period of time, those who become dependent tend to continue to require a great deal of attention, affection, and approval from others. These individuals have difficulty finding comfort even from God's word, and lack inner peace. Friends, family and caregivers may become tired or feel stressed from trying to meet the many needs of the dependent person. Dependent people may look for complete acceptance from everyone they meet and become angry when others do not accept them. They may even borrow a part of a personality from someone close to them, perhaps a co-worker, pastor, or supervisor, having lost sight of their own persona.

What can I do to develop a better sense of independence?

Dependency is complicated and therefore requires skilled intervention, which is well worth the time and effort. Treatment can work for the missionary and family. Restored confidence in God means a renewed sense of direction and freedom for future ministry.

Please take advantage of the resources at the end of this book. They are for you. A computer and internet access make communication with counselors and agencies easier. Your quality of life will improve if you reach out to those who understand some of what you feel.

Learning to fully participate in life and in ministry again can feel like being set free. You may be experiencing a frozen state of insecurity, paralyzed—unable to move forward. Family and friends will welcome you back, healing will happen, hearts will open where you may have thought they were closed.

It is important to develop positive coping skills to allow you to communicate effectively, openly, and honestly with those in your life when you begin rebuilding from a place of dependence. You will make changes that will touch everyone around you, and the new skills will benefit every part of your family, life, and ministry. You are never too old to begin again. "All things are possible with God." (Mark 10:27)

Depression

Over the course of several months we were 'visited' by rebel soldiers and other armed elements; we were robbed of our supplies, our personnel were attacked, and one of our national doctors was killed. We remained, a staff of 80 persons trying to keep a 400 bed hospital open in the midst of war, cut off from the capital city with dwindling supplies, resources and resolve. I didn't recognize it at the time, but

I was experiencing symptoms consistent with depression. I had no appetite, I wasn't sleeping, and nighttime was an occasion to take long walks unseen by others and weep.

What is depression?

Depression is a common symptom for those who have experienced trauma and may influence one's feelings, attitude, and confidence in God. Depression may look like sadness, or a missionary may cover depression with a confident smile making this symptom difficult to detect.

When someone close to you dies, you experience sadness as a normal part of the grieving process. Depression is a typical response to loss, difficulties, and setbacks. Sometimes the feelings of sadness become intense and last much longer than normal grief, causing clinical depression. Depression may not be discussed honestly, because a missionary may believe that depression is a spiritual problem or a sign of character weakness. Depression may be seen as a lack of faith. While our attitudes and beliefs certainly influence our emotions, science tells us clinical depression has a chemical component, a change in the way the chemicals in the brain function. We are still just learning about these chemicals and the medications best used to treat depression, but we have come a long way in the last thirty years.

Genetics also plays a role in determining who will experience depression and how serious the depression will be. Did your mother, father or a sibling suffer from depression or anxiety—and with what medication were they treated? These questions are important to answer when you seek treatment for any of the signs and symptoms presented in this book.

Signs of depression may include a physical slowing or agitation, anxiety, fears, feelings of guilt, hopelessness, frequent crying, withdrawal, difficulty making decisions, low self-esteem, sudden negative view of the world, substance abuse, or thoughts of suicide. Sometimes deep depression actually leads to a suicide attempt. It is very important to get help immediately if you or someone you know ever talks about thoughts of suicide. Suicide is a leading cause of death. When someone suggests they are thinking of suicide, take their words seriously. Have a safety plan ready with a trusted friend, and follow through with your safety plan if ever you feel unsafe.

It is understandable that trauma experienced on the mission field could lead to symptoms of depression. A depressed person may no longer find interest in the things or people once enjoyed. There may be "survivor's guilt" because you came home while others did not. There is no shame in depression. It would be unfortunate not to seek treatment when depression can be successfully treated. There is help and support for you; there is a listening ear for you. Please consult the resources in the back of this book.

What can I do about my symptoms of depression?

Diagnosis and treatment by a qualified professional, a physician, nurse practitioner, or licensed counselor will offer relief to the pain and isolation of depressive symptoms. Learning positive coping skills through counseling will help you feel more control as your depressed mood lifts. Once you feel well enough to begin to exercise, please do so, as this will have the duel benefit of improving both your mood and sleep. It is helpful to eliminate unhealthy habits. In doing this you will notice a positive change in your mood. Your confidence in God, physical and emotional comfort, peace, and contentment will grow.

Success builds on success. Regular counseling is vital and can help you sustain your recovery. Symptoms of depression often respond well to medications. Medications and psychotherapy together are the best treatment for depression. It is critical to take prescribed meds exactly as ordered. Maintain good contact with your medication management provider, counselor and support person. Keep asking questions until you get the answers you need and are feeling better. It is a serious, yet common mistake to stop taking antidepressant medication too soon because you start to feel better and think, "I don't need that pill anymore!" Then, in a matter of time, after stopping the medication, the signs and symptoms of depression return with a vengeance, often more serious than before.

Please, do not make that mistake. Usually it is appropriate to take an antidepressant for at least one year following the first diagnosis of depression. The positive results of symptom relief are worth the effort.

Disordered Eating

I grew up as the "responsible" MK. When I was in seventh grade, my mother had a hysterectomy and came home to recover. Shortly afterward my Dad left for several weeks of traveling to raise funds for the mission. I was left "in charge" of my Mom and sister. Early the next morning, Mom didn't look well. Something inside told me to stay home from school, so I sent Joan off and hung around the house so I could care for our Mom. Suddenly, my mom began to hemorrhage. Feeling panicked, I tried to reach the doctor and several friends, with no luck.

I started crying and praying for help. Finally I reached a friend who was a nurse, and she got in touch with the right medical people to get my Mom back to the hospital. I think that was the day I began to eat everything in sight. I didn't stop until I had gained forty pounds! Food was my comfort. I didn't know any other way to soothe myself…

What is disordered eating?

Poor or unhealthy eating habits may result in a wide variety of physical or emotional concerns. Whatever the cause of poor eating, regaining a healthy diet and regular exercise habits when recovering from trauma is important to the success of a full recovery.

Missionaries who have unhealthy eating habits may be seriously affecting their health. Some adjust well, but all run the risk of physical and emotional complications such as obesity, diabetes, heart disease, stroke, high cholesterol, osteoporosis, and skeletal problems. Emotional difficulties such as anger, anxiety, depression, low self-esteem, guilt, or frustration are frequently experienced by the missionary and family, and these may lead to compensatory eating.

Some overeat as a negative coping skill to cover or "stuff" feelings of stress, anxiety, grief, loneliness, and sadness. The food abuser is literally feeding his or her pain. The trouble is that deep pain cannot be satiated in this way, but only by the Lord's healing with understanding and often, when the injury is deep, the inclusion of professional intervention. The feeling of fullness does not last for long. The hunger will return. There is a feeling of lack of control, pain, self-loathing, more hunger, more pain, and more lack of control.

Some overeaters purge their bodies after eating by vomiting or over-using laxatives. This is called bulimia and requires specific, specialized treatment. Counselors can help with a referral to the appropriate professional. The internet has many websites, but take care to stay with sites that are endorsed by reputable medical and psychiatric professionals, because treatment of eating disorders generally requires the help of a physician, psychiatric nurse practitioner, nutritionist, and mental health professional. This is why you are encouraged to begin with Christian counselors who have training in eating disorders.

What can I do to recover from disordered eating?

Gaining insight into why one overeats is a process. People need to learn about why they crave unhealthy foods, and what triggers binge overeating. They need to want to make changes knowing that it will not be easy. With the help of a nutritionist, you will find a food plan that works for your lifestyle. Remember, you are in this for the long-haul, not for a quick fix and a return to bad habits. You may find you feel better when you avoid eating when you are anxious, between meals, or after 7 p.m.

All major habit changes require courage, determination, time and God's strength. A counselor's support will help you retake control of a schedule, daily activities, and food habits. Also, take a look at exercise habits, consider walking daily, and develop an exercise plan that will work specifically for you. Share your thoughts and feelings with significant others in your life and ask for help. This can be hard and this can be humbling. Tell them how important it is they respect the new eating plan that is a matter of health for you and ask they not discourage you by bringing home foods that tempt you, at least in the beginning. This is an area where family communication is very important. Education about what is really happening matters for the people with whom you live and share your life.

Read about foods to learn about calorie content, carbohydrates, hidden calories and chemicals, and the different types of fats. You may be surprised by what is really in some of your favorite foods. Try rewarding yourself in non-food related ways when you experience success. Increase social interactions with positive peers, make positive statements to yourself from scripture, and talk to yourself encouragingly. Remember that God made you in his image, and you want to glorify him by learning self-control and giving your body healthy food and exercise.

Abuse of food can hinder the testimony of one to another, not to mention lowering self-confidence. If food is abused in any way, there is help and understanding within your mental health community. If available in your region, Overeaters Anonymous (OA) is an effective support group for individuals with food issues. If you do not get the support or answers you need, keep asking until you do. Good health is worth recovering if lost. A healthy, glowing person is inside, waiting to break free. Believe—and know that if believing in recovery seems too difficult right now, there are people of faith who will be strong and believe *for you* during treatment.

Flashbacks

Throughout my life I've had disconnected moments. I've looked into the mirror and not recognized my own face, even when I have seen it looking back at me. I've had the feeling I'm viewing the traumatic experience, the moment of abuse, from above, as it happened—and not actually being part of it—I am just "floating" during the flashback. There have been many anxiety attacks, irrational fears, and times of feeling paralyzed both physically and emotionally.

What are flashbacks?

A flashback is a timeless instant taking a person back to the moment of trauma, where one least wants to go. The human brain is a powerful and an amazing machine—miraculous, complex, and at times confounding. We are just beginning to understand how the brain works. The flashback may represent unfinished business, difficult choices, unacceptable solutions, or an attempt to master something beyond the control of the conscious mind.

The individual experiencing flashback symptoms may be unaware of what triggers the event. It may be the noises of children playing, a loud bang, the smell of a dead animal, a particular color, or the sound of a foreign language. Suddenly, the person feels displaced. He or she may feel out of control, unable to trust the body to respond. The life-long assumption of safety has vanished. Everything once trusted is suddenly gone. The body is paralyzed—in a frozen state.

This is a frightening way to live because you can be whisked away unexpectedly, in your mind, to a different place. You may hear the term "dissociate," which is to be in one place physically but not present emotionally. Some mental health professionals believe the brain is protecting itself by dissociating from a traumatic incident too difficult to fully experience at the time of the occurrence, and the flashback is an attempt to resolve the trauma more slowly. One symptom in the diagnosis of post-traumatic stress is this timeless state in which you are an involuntary witness to your traumatic past.

What can I do to cope with flashbacks?

Flashbacks do *not* have to control your life. With God's help and the counsel of professionals, you can learn to trust your mind again. It is crucial to discover your triggers to flashbacks or dissociative moments. These black holes of fear must be replaced with God's comfort and peace. When you have worked through your reasons for having experienced flashbacks you will begin to notice healthy emotions return as you find your "new normal."

Paul was imprisoned by his enemies; your *enemy* may be recurring flashbacks. Remember, "I can do everything through him who gives me strength."(Phil. 4:13) Consider making a goal of holding the memories in your conscious mind. This is not an easy task and will be a long-term goal. A supportive counselor can help you in the process. God will provide the encouragement and strength you need to reach your goal if you ask him.

Every symptom listed in this book has common *triggers* that make symptoms more severe. Some triggers will likely be obvious to you, and others are more obvious to those around you. It is important to practice becoming receptive when told a trigger has affected your mood negatively. This feedback (information given back to you) may be hard to hear at first—you may not want to listen or talk about it, but you may appreciate this knowledge when avoiding the trigger prevents change in mood to the point of flashback. Eventually you will begin to feel a greater sense of peace and healing.

Grief

When our child was sent to a boarding school in another country, I broke down in tears and experienced long periods of sorrow. The separation was made more difficult by the boarding school's policy discouraging phone calls. Each time we called to communicate with our child, we were near tears. I was depressed and lonely. Eventually, I felt completely immobilized.

What is grief?
Grief is a totally normal, healthy response to an experience of loss, separation, or death. Christ taught his disciples, "Blessed are those who mourn, for they will be comforted." (Matt. 5:4) Mourning, weeping, sadness, and tears are a natural, God-given way to express grief and sorrow. Everyone has a personal response to death or loss and no response is wrong. Some will recover quickly, but some feel symptoms of grief for what seems like a very long time.

The healing process of grieving seems a bit easier to walk through with support. Different cultures have ceremonious ways to remember and honor the dead. These expressions vary among nationalities within every culture. Burial ceremonies are useful societal tools for the expressions of grief and loss. The funeral experience can help with closure. After a funeral or memorial service, the grieving process may take a year or two to complete its natural course.

Missionaries serving in times of war and political upheaval may have inadequate time to stop for the grief process to run its course. Symptoms of shock, anger, pain, sadness, guilt, and denial may begin to grow within the individual who has not been able to grieve. Sometimes grief is postponed for months or even years. In these cases, it is important to take time to discuss those unresolved losses buried in your memory with a trusted friend, pastor, or counselor. Remembering these losses and talking about them should help begin your healing process.

Physical symptoms of grief may include increased heart rate, a lump in the throat, crying often or suddenly, dizziness, intestinal upset or nausea, loss of appetite, fatigue, poor attention, or sleep difficulties. Denial is a common symptom of grief associated with the post-trauma experience, especially when the missionary is still in a critical environment and cannot let down emotionally for safety reasons. For a while it seems easier to pretend there has been no loss or to be angry at the loved one or fallen friend than to cope with the loss.

It is important to debrief and ask for help as soon as possible after a critical incident, death, or a significant loss. You do not have to suffer alone.

What can I do with my grief?

Learning to cope with grief takes time. Making that first call for help or logging on to a computer to access sources may be your first step to connecting with help. Talking about your feelings is important, as well as discussing with a pastor or counselor the theology of suffering. Understanding why the pain has become overwhelming can put you on the road to healing.

Healthy life skills are very important during times of grief. Eat a balanced diet, exercise, learn and practice good sleep hygiene, keep a regular routine, spend extra time in prayer and worship, explore a hobby you will enjoy, and try to be around people you like. Avoid making major decisions while still grieving, and allow yourself time to cry. Sometimes men are discouraged from crying by the norms of society. Even if it is in a locked room, men need to be supported and encouraged to shed healing tears if they so choose.

Although you believe in eternal life, angry feelings are understandable when someone dies, especially when the death is unexpected. Pastors, counselors, medical providers and funeral directors are trained to answer the nagging questions experienced by those facing loss. It is often better to know the truth than to entertain your imagination.

A written safety plan is a great idea if you are having feelings of harming yourself because your grief has caused you to feel depressed. (See section on safety plans). Talk to someone at the first thought of self-harm. Have your safety plan ready. Taking your own life is never the answer. Your life will go on as you learn to trust those God has put in your path to support you.

Guilt

My husband and I were responsible for supervising a class trip of twenty-three missionary kids on a school retreat off the coast of Ecuador. During a day of swimming at the ocean, the youngest member of the class was swept out to sea. My husband, a strong swimmer, nearly drowned as he battled strong waves to rescue Jimmy. The student was literally torn from my husband's grasp and washed into eternity. We were overwhelmed with guilt and sorrow. Guilt meant taking responsibility for what transpired. Shame meant facing Jimmy's parents and the other missionaries. -Kay

What is guilt?

Guilt is the feeling of a strong sense of remorse that results from believing you have done something wrong. Missionaries may carry guilt for many years from service-related experiences. "Survivor's guilt" is common among accident victims and missionaries who have come home having survived when peers have suffered or died. Feelings that accompany guilt may be shame, disgrace, embarrassment, regret, insecurity, anxiety, low self-esteem, or anger.

Guilt may color the way a person sees God, self, and the world. When something goes tragically wrong, the missionary may feel deserted by God. It may become difficult to relate to your family and community when experiencing the burden of guilt and your ministry may be affected. Feelings of remorse may make it difficult to be "yourself" in social situations, where before, you enjoyed positive, healthy relationships.

Guilt may be the result of feeling you should have done something differently, when in reality, there may have been no choice. You may feel like a failure, and choose to punish yourself by isolating from those who would support and love you. There are some who refuse help because to feel better would dishonor the lost. We all deserve to talk to someone who understands something of what we have been through, whether the incident is recent or happened many, many years ago.

Many survivors of political revolutions, war, violence, or near-death experiences feel the burden of emotional guilt for many reasons. With support, counseling, and time you will learn to recognize *triggers* to feelings of guilt. It is important to recognize guilt triggers to figure out how to avoid them. Avoiding triggers will, in time, lessen feelings of guilt. You will learn to forgive yourself and perhaps others. It is critical to walk with Christ to accept forgiveness. Only then will you learn to regain a full and loving life in this wonderful ministry for which you have dedicated a part of your life in service.

As you educate yourself, pray, and share with a trusted friend, you will begin to recognize and understand the physical symptoms that may occur when guilt surfaces. These symptoms include increased pulse rate, flushed face, or the urge to pace, isolate, or lash out in anger.

What can I do to cope with my feelings of guilt?

You can learn healthy communication skills to better express your guilt and other feelings as you recover. You will learn to prepare a safety plan should you feel unsafe toward yourself or anyone else.

Prescription medication may help you relax or improve your sleep if sleep has been affected on a short-term basis or decrease symptoms of depression often associated with guilt. Talk with your counselor about a medication management referral if your symptoms do not improve with talk therapy. The symptoms of trauma you are experiencing *are treatable*.

Please honor the Lord, your family, and you by talking to someone. Utilize any of the resources from the back of this book. Know from this moment that you are not alone. You are never alone—never (Ps. 23).

Isolation/avoidance/withdrawal

I was completely burned out. At the end of the term I was totally spent. I didn't want to be around people. I had trouble engaging, even with my family. We adopted our second child around this time, but I had no energy. Throughout our entire furlough I was tired continually and even into our next term of service, I was exhausted. I suffered ongoing feelings of despair, depression, regret, and unworthiness.

What is isolation?

Isolation, avoidance and withdrawal are marked by *alone-ness* from those who would offer support to the missionary or family member.

Sadly, when the missionary separates from community, the whole family is separated as well. The isolating missionary may have poor ability relating to others, and so relationships break down within and throughout the family and community.

Missionaries may feel exhausted, overwhelmed, and preoccupied with memories of their traumatic experiences. As a result, they may have difficulty sharing feelings such as anger, sadness, grief or guilt. Wanting to be alone, missionaries may eventually shut themselves off completely, avoiding those who would offer support.

Consequences of withdrawn and isolative behavior are that family, friends, and ministry may suffer as well as the individual and family. People may then avoid the one who suffers, not understanding the behavior, which can set up a cycle of rejection and pain. The withdrawn behavior may be mistaken as hostility, brooding anger, or rudeness.

Concerned family and friends may reach out to a counselor on behalf of the isolated individual, but it must be up to the person in need to be open to treatment. This can be difficult to accept.

What can I do to change my withdrawn behavior?

You will become more socially active when you discover what is behind your desire to withdraw from life. Your counselor will offer education about how you can learn to practice activities as you regain confidence in God and in you. Your interest in life and in others will increase over time. Positive coping skills begin by learning to focus on awareness of why and when you began to isolate in the first place. Is the behavior related to circumstances on the mission field? Are you responding to internal stimuli such as voices or racing thoughts? Are you afraid of relationships? The more information and understanding you have about the causes of your behavior, the less withdrawn you will likely be.

It will take some time to regain trust. In time, sharing in a group may be beneficial to the healing process. Talking to missionaries who have experienced burn out and periods of isolation can be a wonderfully encouraging experience. It helps to realize that nobody is alone, and that others in ministry have also overcome trying times.

"Two are better than one, because they have good return for their work. If one falls down, his friend can help him up." Eccles. 4:9, 10.

Loneliness

For years I was the "invisible" person and didn't know how to handle it when people remembered me from my years of service in South America. My relationships had suffered. I began to wonder "What is love?" Could I really allow myself to feel things emotionally anymore? I was dead inside; it was easier to remain invisible.

What is loneliness?

Loneliness is a lack of intimacy on many levels. There may be a profound feeling of lack of support, a feeling of indifference and "aloneness," with no one to whom the sufferer can turn in his unchosen solitude. Lack of intimacy may lead to emotional isolation, which then leads to social isolation. Loneliness is a symptom of trauma, one of the most commonly expressed by those who have been through profound loss. As a result of ongoing loneliness the individual may also notice symptoms of depressed mood, anxiety, and various physical illnesses.

It is impossible to underestimate the impact of living in the shadow of loneliness. The missionary, MK, or family member may be completely surrounded by loving family or friends but feel very much alone. Loneliness can make it more difficult to live and work in a positive state of mind. Feelings may include dread, desperation, restlessness, emptiness, anxiety, low self-esteem, indifference, sadness, or suicidal thoughts. Loneliness may be the result of losses or disturbing events in the person's life.

Loneliness may surface around the anniversary dates of a trauma the missionary or individual has experienced. The anniversary date is, therefore, the *trigger* to experiencing the loneliness. This reliving of the event through memories may come as a surprise to the individual, and may become a dreaded and expected yearly occurrence. Specific triggers can make symptoms of loneliness more difficult to bear. Even a change in season may act as a trigger with the change in temperature, smells, or appearance of foliage reminding you of the season when a trauma occurred.

When you are lonely, physical symptoms such as headache, backache, nausea, or other intestinal symptoms seem worse and may actually become worse. Missionaries experiencing long-term loneliness may begin to have barriers to communication such as speech and hearing deficits. Feeling overwhelmed with loneliness, a missionary may unwisely seek immediate relief in the companionship of someone who has a negative influence or is dangerous. Sometimes it seems easier to share lonely feelings with a stranger. This can lead to further isolation, physical danger, pain, legal difficulties and disease.

What can I do to cope with my feelings of loneliness?

Talking to a pastor, counselor, or confidential friend can help you learn to recognize the physical symptoms of loneliness. When you are lonely, you can realistically lessen the uncomfortable symptoms if you learn to practice good sleeping habits and learn relaxation skills. Reduce caffeine, limit alcohol intake, do not use illegal drugs, avoid self-destructive behavior, and consider beginning a hobby you enjoy.

One of several ways to begin to learn these skills is to ask someone who has already taken the first step—another missionary who has worked through some of the pain of reintegration into their homeland. Missionaries and those who support them can learn how to get in touch with someone who has taken their first step by using some of the resources in this book. Consider attending individual or group psychotherapy sessions to talk about feelings of loneliness. It is often difficult to imagine attending a "therapy" or "support group," but those who follow through with attending have a better opportunity to improve and heal.

In treatment you will figure out what triggers lonely feelings. You will learn ways to feel God's presence, to see him as your faithful friend who is always with you. When feeling lonely and down, find comfort in God's word, meditation, prayer, and fellowship. Learn how to write a crisis plan to use in case of emergency. This is much like a safety plan and will represent the names and numbers to call first in time of crisis. In your plan you will identify a support system to use if feelings of loneliness become overwhelming, or if feelings of powerlessness lead to dangerous feelings of becoming unsafe toward yourself or someone else.

As you learn to trust others and to share honestly, in time your feelings of loneliness will fade. You will learn ways to maintain positive and fulfilling relationships. Please take this time to take the first step.

Low Self-esteem/negative Self-concept

I felt betrayed by the staff—people in whom I put all my energy. Sometimes I felt like a failure, like I didn't accomplish what I thought I should have as a missionary. At times I've been numb, unable to concentrate, lethargic, and depressed.

What is low self esteem?

A negative self-concept means believing that you are not quite good enough. Self-identity is not positive and abilities, capabilities, worth, intelligence, or appearance are in question. It is hard to see the future in a positive light, because your view of self is not as God sees you, or even as others may see you. Often the individual with a negative self-concept will not "give themselves a break." Low self-esteem is not the same as humility, which is a God-given trait. Low self-esteem is underestimating one's self worth, and may find its roots within the family of origin, during childhood or adolescence, or as the result of failure experienced in early adult life. Wherever the origin of negative self-thought, it is important for your future to begin to see *self* as valuable, important, individual, unique and unconditionally loved by God.

Negative self-concept colors life because everyday tasks lack joy and enthusiasm. Expecting rejection creates lack of trust and fear. The body image will suffer when living in fear, and irrational fears may increase without support, encouragement and treatment.

Low self-esteem often leads to feelings of inferiority, incompetence, inadequacy, and failure. Missionaries may become frustrated and discouraged. Negative thoughts and feelings may lead to the point of dropping out of ministry, or even considering ending their lives—suicide. Thoughts of suicide must *always* be taken seriously. Go to the nearest trusted person for help right away; talk to someone if you are having thoughts of ending your life. Asking for help is a sign of wisdom.

God created every human being as a unique and special person, and he will guide everyone's life and work individually. Setbacks in missionary life may occur and God can use these events to teach valuable life lessons through the suffering we may experience. He wants us to have an accurate view of ourselves, one of "sober judgment" (Rom. 12:3). You will learn with help and support, to love yourself the way God loves you, maybe for the first time, maybe again, unconditionally and eternally.

What can I do to have a healthy self concept?

Learning to recognize what has brought about low self-concept is sometimes uncomfortable, but worth the search. In time, learning to accept your body, mind, and spirit as they are will bring peace and comfort. Finding ways to improve self, relationships, and performance in a healthy and constructive way, will further build self-esteem.

As part of treatment, a counselor may encourage you to verbalize feelings to help you recognize your strengths, skills, and assets. Confidence is regained as you practice making accurate and positive statements about self. Learn how to overcome discouragement and setbacks as your self-worth and self-esteem increase. Individual counseling and group sharing can be very helpful as you gain insight.

Prescriptive medication may be useful if anxiety, depression or other symptoms are affecting your outlook as you seek relief from symptoms of post-traumatic stress.

Obsessions

*I went through a few months when I was obsessed with the thought
that I wasn't saved. I would pray the sinner's prayer over and over, often
dozens of times a day, hoping that God heard me. I felt that I had no
assurance that my salvation was secure. How could this simple prayer get
me into heaven? The thought that scared me was that I would die, and
God would tell me that I just hadn't done enough to get into heaven.*

What are obsessions?

Obsessions are persistent and recurring thoughts, ideas, impulses, images,
or urges that permeate consciousness. Obsessions become involuntary,
seem to have a life of their own and become central to the thought process.
Like unwanted pop-ups on a computer screen, obsessions intrude into the
mind and are difficult to delete. Obsessions vary in intensity; therefore,
these thoughts can disturb missionaries who suffer from obsessions to
varying degrees.

Treatment takes time and patience. There is a reason you are thinking
this way and others are available to offer help, encouragement and support.

Common obsessions include germs, disgust of bodily waste, concern
about odor, worry about the order or symmetry of objects, and thoughts of
harming someone. There may be obsessions about sinful thoughts, images,
words, or numbers. Usually the sufferer understands the thoughts are
unreasonable and becomes frustrated by them. Obsessions can occur at the
same time with depression and other symptoms such as anxiety, phobias,
and panic disorders. It is easy to understand why obsessions exist when you
read about these symptoms of trauma.

What can I do to cope with my obsessions?

Christian counselors will assist you as you move past your life of
obsessions. You will learn to rethink situations that have triggered anxiety
and repetitive behavior until the obsessions diminish over time. Once you
have learned personal triggers to events that cause obsessions to surface,
you will be able to regain control and overcome feelings of anxiety. Positive
coping skills, thought-stopping techniques, and scripture verses to fill your
mind are helpful tools in overcoming obsessive thoughts. Have patience and
allow yourself to make mistakes as you begin to see the world differently.
A counselor will help you find the support needed to cope effectively with
obsessive thoughts. You may not recognize the supports you already have.

Obsessions can dominate your life if you do not regain a more healthy and balanced kind of control. Treatment and time can help you recover control of your "mental computer." Your life, family, and ministry will improve as a result. The torment of the past can heal when obsessions eventually diminish. You will experience God's comfort and peace. You will be able to take charge of your mind and emotions in a different, more positive way, maybe for the first time.

Paranoia/hypervigilance

After I was sexually assaulted, I found myself looking over my shoulder all the time. I would take great lengths not to be alone in the dark, not to drive alone without the doors locked, and never to walk alone in solitary places. Every stranger was my enemy, someone to look out for. I didn't trust men at all.

What is paranoia?

Paranoia is a haunting feeling of mistrust. Paranoia, a term also used diagnostically, is an ongoing feeling that someone is after you, and may involve other intrusive thoughts. Paranoia can interfere with every aspect of life. You may fear intimacy and isolate yourself. The missionary may move away from family, friends, and all supports in an effort to find safety because of suspicions and paranoid feelings. In fact, being alone can increase the feelings of paranoia. Anxiety, depression, and other symptoms of having experienced trauma require support and understanding. Without intervention, fear from memories and trauma of the past may haunt the missionary for a long time.

Hypervigilance is a form of high alert where you are on the lookout for threats in your environment. You are hypersensitive to any signs of these perceived threats. While this level of alert is a survival skill learned in stressful situations and is protective during crisis, it may continue for years after safety is restored. It sometimes presents as a startle reaction.

Missionaries and MKs may experience physical symptoms such as headaches, nausea, increased heart rate, and other symptoms. The body is working overtime; the body has become accustomed to functioning at an escalated rate. Survivors may imagine someone is trying to harm them. When you present your symptoms to a professional, you will need trained clinical support to teach you relaxation skills. Medication may also be necessary for a period of time. Consult a licensed independent provider for medication management and take a family member or trusted friend with you into your appointment. It is a good thing to have someone with you who knows about you, who can describe your mood before and after the trauma. Ask questions and take notes, or ask your friend to do so.

To help you function better in daily life, a counselor will determine how the symptoms developed, and teach you how to restore faith in God's protection and safety. It is important to learn why suspicion or paranoia began. If the cause of unhealthy thinking is trauma or you are experiencing symptoms associated with trauma, it is critical to gain this information, which is where insight begins.

What can I do to cope with paranoia?

Learn positive coping skills to avoid letting suspicion or paranoia control your life. Lowering the stress and triggers to agitation in your life is important to begin the healing process. It is very helpful to learn how to relax, meditate on the Lord, and let the Holy Spirit's peace minister.

One important indicator of progress is the development of a trusting relationship with your counselor. This is called a *therapeutic relationship*, and is sometimes the first honest, trusting relationship a trauma survivor has ever had. Confidence will grow as the counseling process proceeds. You will experience a stronger sense of safety and better understand why you are feeling paranoid or hypervigilant. In time, the suspicions will fade.

Please remember to update your medical health when there is a sudden change in mood or thought, to be sure there are no contributing medical conditions. (This is the responsibility of your primary care provider). With work, support, time, and good communication between your providers, you can recover to an improved quality of life.

Passive-aggressive Behavior

Why doesn't Gary tell me the truth about what he needs? He shuts down emotionally and doesn't communicate with me or the kids. Everyone knows he's mad about something, but he denies it. All of us feel the tension and it's just not fair.

What is passive-aggressive behavior?

Passive-aggressive behavior is an indirect verbal or non-verbal method of communication. People may express emotions of anger and hostility covertly instead of speaking overtly and honestly. It is a provocative way of communicating. Passive-aggressive behavior sends mixed messages, stirs up fear, and may create strain in relationships.

Passive-aggressiveness can cause emotional problems such as depression, anxiety, or anger-management problems if healthy communication skills are not developed in order to effectively express feelings. This behavior can create conflicts with co-workers and family, which can lead to frustration and emotional as well as physical violence. Passive-aggressive behavior is extremely damaging to marriages. Passive-aggressive behavior eventually will separate family and peers.

Some passive-aggressive comments are mildly sarcastic; examples are easily available on TV sitcoms. Others are seemingly calm and cooperative but hide anger and rage from trauma suffered in the past. Some people become passive-aggressive because they are afraid to honestly admit how they feel.

How can I learn to communicate without using passive-aggressive behaviors?

There is always room for improving communication skills and learning how to honestly express feelings. Just as Proverbs 12:17 says, "A truthful witness gives honest testimony," telling the truth about what you need and how you feel helps others know they can trust your word. Honest communication helps others know how to respond.

It is essential to seek professional help to learn the causes behind passive-aggressive behaviors. Only then can you understand the behavior and work to change. It is important to identify triggers to these behaviors and learn how to express yourself in a positive way. Then and only then will your relationships begin to improve.

Physical responses to passive-aggressive behaviors may include headache, increased heart rate, or increased volume of voice. Good boundaries and assertive skills will help you to communicate in a positive, non-aggressive, and polite manner in order to get your needs met. Learn to walk away from any situation that causes you to feel threatened. Think instead about an appropriate, mature response. You will be more apt to be heard when you use effective leadership skills.

Phobia

I had flown on airplanes all my life, but after I suffered a physical attack, I developed a fear of flying. The strange thing about my phobia

*was that it didn't seem connected to the trauma I was now experiencing.
Yet, I had no other explanation for my new-found fear. Weeks before a
scheduled flight, I tried to think of any other way to get to my intended
destination. Often I canceled a flight or drove; sometimes it would
mean several extra days of travel. In my mind I could see airplanes
falling from the sky. The night before a flight, I didn't sleep a wink, but
paced the bedroom floor in a cold, anxious sweat. I had to muster all
my inner strength to get on a plane. The phobia lasted for about four
years, until I had no choice but to figure out a way to conquer the fear.
I chose to fly nearly every day for a week! By the end of that week, I
started to feel better about getting on airplanes.*

What is a phobia?

Phobias are disturbing thoughts of varying intensity, frightening at times,
of an object, activity, or situation. A person with a phobia consciously
avoids the feared situation, and experiences heightened anxiety if the
person cannot avoid the phobia. It is common for a phobia to develop after
a missionary has been exposed to an upsetting, life-threatening situation.
The phobia may be linked to a prior trauma, or may develop into a fear of
something unrelated. This fear often has a small grain of truth or reality, but
the likelihood of it happening is greatly exaggerated.

Some phobias are common and, although they are annoying, may be
tolerable. Others are dysfunctional and interfere with life to varying degrees.
A phobia may become so intense the sufferer cannot leave home for fear
of coming into contact with the object. Common phobias include fear
of snakes, mice, or spiders. Phobias associated with missionaries include
fears of flying, contamination from germs, crowds, sudden movements, or
loud noises. Phobias may interfere with ministry and personal life as fear
intensifies. The sufferer may feel such a loss of control that isolation from
others seems a reasonable choice. This may then lead to feelings of paranoia,
depression, anxiety, loneliness, helplessness, powerlessness, or inadequacy.

Missionaries with phobias may blame themselves for not trusting
God *enough* or not having faith to overcome their fears. Self-blame can
hinder them from seeking professional treatment. Phobias are frightening
and are successfully treated through gradual exposure to the feared
object or situation, along with relaxation skills and coping techniques.
With counseling and treatment you will gain insight so you will not feel
overwhelmed or scared. Your faith and confidence will return. Gradually,
phobias will lose their power.

What can I do to cope with my phobia?

It is important to learn to cope with a phobia in order to reclaim emotional control. Learn ways to adapt to everyday stressors that may be making a phobia more powerful. Learn the triggers to a phobia and with prayer, support, and courage take back control of your emotions. Identify the link between phobias and anxiety. Work on social skills so anxiety lessens and confidence grows when interacting with others.

Counselors offer supportive guidance to begin the healing process, including a referral to a physician should medication become necessary. Remember, give yourself time! Phobias may have a sudden onset, but time helps the mind to return to a place of safety.

Secondary Traumatic Stress Disorder

What is Secondary Traumatic Stress Disorder?

Those who in some way have been associated with survivors of trauma may also become traumatized and experience what is called secondary traumatic stress disorder (STSD), or compassion fatigue. Traumatic experiences, war, prolonged stressful work, and discouraging setbacks may break down the trusted relationships of the missionary. This creates increased stress on the spiritual, psychological, and physical capacities of the person whose life-long coping skills may have been shattered by traumas and disillusionment. The missionary may no longer know how to act or what to expect in order to function effectively.

People in the missionary's life, especially spouses, children, and extended family, may begin to exhibit characteristics or symptoms similar to post-traumatic stress, just by living with the missionary's post-traumatic symptoms. Children who were not actually born when the missionary served on the mission field may also exhibit STSD. Children of some missionaries, who have the diagnosis PTSD and other mental health diagnoses, exhibit impaired self-esteem, hyperactivity, poor reality testing, and aggressive behavior. They may have difficulty coping with guilt, fear, rage and feelings of mistrust. It's a form of "referred pain," passed on unknowingly by the traumatized person.

Those who study traumatology recognize that care givers who interact in any manner with trauma survivors are, themselves, exposed to traumatic stressors. As you read this book, you are learning about signs and symptoms related to post-traumatic stress and the diagnostic criteria as defined by the DSM-IV. The symptoms for Secondary Traumatic Stress may be familiar and yet feel so strange and unexpected. The family member, peer, health caregiver, or anyone associated with a missionary or MK diagnosed with PTS may need perspective and support.

Whenever there is trauma, there is pain and need for education, healing, and guidance. As with Post-Traumatic Stress, awareness that you or a loved one may suffer from the symptoms of Secondary Trauma, and that you are not the first, is an important step. For some, this recognition brings about a welcome reframing of one's world. For others, seeking treatment after having supported the missionary for some time may be a great relief and may move the family unit toward greater peace, comfort, and healing. Untreated STSD may lead to more extreme reactions and eventual development of chronic symptoms and a PTSD diagnosis.

The most common characteristics of PTSD are:

- visualization—flashbacks, the ability to recall, see in the mind's eye, a terrible event or trauma;
- reenactment—the trauma unconsciously acted out, to restore power and control;
- fear of intimacy, pain, or loss of control;
- victimization associated with relationships;
- a sense of hopelessness—trauma has taught the lesson that at any moment safety could be destroyed.

Any of these "common characteristics" and any of the post-trauma symptoms described in this book may also be seen in a person suffering from Secondary Trauma on some level.

What can I do about Secondary Traumatic Stress Disorder?

If you recognize any of these symptoms in someone, it is important to understand there is treatment and support available for Secondary Traumatic Stress. As you read, you will recognize and understand some of the symptoms. At the back of the book are references and resources to increase your knowledge, and to help you find counselors and supporters in your region of the world.

We hope the information offered in these pages will shed light on your symptoms. Improving your quality of life is essential. You deserve to heal just as the missionary in your life deserves your support and encouragement. God's healing, restoration, and peace are the goals for everyone.

Sexual Trauma

As an MK, I was sexually, emotionally, physically, and spiritually abused by both house parents in the dorm where I lived. I was raped repeatedly for two years. The abuse, in my case, ended only when the house parents suddenly left the field. I've since had anxiety attacks, irrational fears, and felt paralyzed physically and emotionally. I fear I will never be completely over it.

What is sexual trauma?

Sexual trauma is a term for uninvited sexual contact or sexual intercourse against a person's will from which the victim has not emotionally recovered. The trauma from the event has remained. Sexual trauma is listed among the symptoms of post-trauma because of the number of missionaries and third culture kids who have experienced some form of sexual abuse. When sexual abuse occurs, the victim may not report the incident due to embarrassment, guilt, or shame. The missionary or child may not receive medical, psychological, or spiritual treatment.

Rape may include the use of force, threat, or intimidation, with vaginal or anal penetration and lack of consent by the person who is assaulted. Sexual abuse happens to both males and females with victims experiencing inappropriate touching, unwanted looking, sexual comments and gestures. The perpetrator, or person responsible for the abuse, may be a friend, relative, a trusted associate, or someone in a position of authority. Sexual predators are often very clever at concealing their actions, and may appear as "normal" as anyone else in a position of trust. When the perpetrator is also a Christian or fellow missionary, the impact of the trauma is spiritually confusing and devastatingly painful. Sexual abuse can negatively change one's view of God, missionaries, and those who serve the Lord.

Recovery from sexual abuse is a slow process. Statistics show the best outcomes occur with support, spiritual counsel, and psychotherapy. Without someone to talk to, the victim may find that symptoms worsen and may include mood instability and flashbacks with memories of the event. It may be extremely difficult to learn to trust anyone after sexual abuse. Fear of developing close relationships may unknowingly sabotage the relationships you manage to form. Fear of intimacy may develop; sexual experiences can become frightening, confusing and frustrating. Some sexual abuse victims become promiscuous.

Those who have suffered sexual abuse may have trouble sleeping, abuse substances such as prescription drugs or alcohol, have trouble with outbursts of anger, or have poor judgment skills. Lack of confidence in God, mistrust of others, and poor self-esteem are common.

How can I recover from sexual trauma?

To say it is difficult to cope with rape is a vast understatement. It is very important to seek professional help as soon as possible after the assault. Choose someone who is educated about sexual abuse, who knows how to minister to someone who has been sexually assaulted, and preferably someone of your own gender.

If you have been sexually abused and have had no assistance, please call or email a resource in the back of this book. Do not delay! Your quality of life will begin to change when you make that call. It will take time, and it will not always be easy, but you will begin to see changes as you counsel with those who care about you. You will learn to overcome memories and powerful emotions. You will learn to believe the rape was not your fault. You will become aware of coping skills to help you begin to sleep better, avoid substance use, or express feelings of anger and frustration in a safe manner. It will help you to talk about the feelings of anxiety, resentment, sadness, guilt, depression, or rage with a counselor and perhaps, in time, in a group with others who understand. You can learn to love and trust the Lord again. You will be glad you did the work to get to that point of healing.

Sleep Disorders

Jill was a missionary intern in a developed country in Eastern Europe where she felt generally safe. One afternoon she was followed to her apartment by a man who grabbed and fondled her in open daylight. The man tried to force his way through her apartment's security gate, but she slammed the door on him and screamed and he ran away. For months afterwards she couldn't sleep at night. She woke up frequently with nightmares and sensations of fear.

What are sleep disorders?

When a person is diagnosed with a sleep disorder, it means they either sleep too much, which is called hypersomnia, or they cannot sleep much at all, called insomnia. Disordered sleep can begin as a slight problem and *gather steam* along with any of the other post-trauma symptoms. A confirmed diagnosis of PTSD almost certainly means you will have a sleep disturbance of some sort, which may help to explain why you are not sleeping soundly.

Most adults benefit from about eight hours of sleep every night and lack energy when they begin going to bed too late or staying in bed too long. Within the missionary population, sleep disturbance may be triggered by experiencing a shocking or violent event or by lack of sleep while adjusting to a new lifestyle following a move. Sleep disorders have physical and emotional symptoms, which may include racing thoughts, nightmares, rapid heart rate, night sweats, headache, nausea, or other symptoms of anxiety as the body struggles to get to sleep or refrain from sleeping too much.

If you begin to lack energy, yawn frequently throughout the day, feel the need to nap or cannot stay awake, you may suffer from a sleep disorder. Seek treatment. Please do not wait. It is important to discover the root cause.

How can I recover from sleep disorders?

With all the signs and symptoms reviewed in this book, getting a clear diagnostic picture from a qualified provider is important. You may need to see more than one professional to get the right treatment or to find the provider who *suits* you. Educating yourself about sleep disorders will help you find the answers you need.

Finding the cause of a sleep disorder is key to working on the cure. To better cope with insomnia, avoid caffeine, alcohol, and other mood-altering substances. For both insomnia and hypersomnia, try gentle exercise, write in a journal about your feelings, draw or paint creatively, pray and meditate on scripture, listen to worship music, take a walk a couple of hours before bed, or enjoy a pet. Eat dinner a bit earlier in the evening, and do not eat or drink more than a little bit after 7 p.m. (Some find if they do not drink liquids after 6 p.m. they no longer awaken at night). If you are near a medical facility, consider physical therapy, hydrotherapy, or massage. Short-term medications may be useful as well.

A set of coping skills referred to as "sleep hygiene" are similar for insomnia and hypersomnia. Make sure your sleeping environment is comfortable and conducive to sleep. Avoid long naps in the afternoon. Develop a regular pattern for bedtime. Learning new sleep patterns takes patience and is best done slowly while you are retraining your brain for healthy sleep. The goal for sleep disorders is good sleep quality with a regular sleep cycle to increase energy and boost good health. Remember, if you lie in bed without sleeping for twenty minutes, get up, do something, and then go back to bed, hopefully for good, quality sleep.

Ask the Lord to send you his peace and the comfort of the Holy Spirit at bedtime. Meditate on this verse: "I will lie down and sleep in peace, for you alone, O Lord, make me dwell in safety" (Ps. 4:8).

Spiritual Confusion

How could God let my colleague die? What was God thinking? My co-worker was a better, more holy person than I... Nothing felt completely real when I tried to make sense of her death. Confusion and doubt washed over me in great waves. If she could die so suddenly, were any of us safe? Was it possible I had missed God's direction and call in my life? I honestly felt that my theology about the Lord's protection would never again be the same.

What is spiritual confusion?

Traumatic events experienced by missionaries may cause them to question their fundamental spiritual beliefs, sense of meaning, Christian foundation, purpose, hope, and faith. Everything thought of as "normal" may be abruptly challenged and altered by tragedy. Traumatic events that are sudden, unexpected, and life-threatening may cause missionaries to question their core beliefs about God and their trust in other people, even those closest to them.

Common spiritual symptoms reported by those experiencing trauma include an altered world view about God's plan, his ways of working in the world, and his personal protection. Missionaries may also grapple with existential questions about suffering, evil, forgiveness, justice, purpose, and God's divine order. They may ask, "Why did God allow this to happen? Does God still care about me?" At times there may be a loss of the sense of meaning in their missionary work, with troubling doubts about what life is all about. These doubts may cause discouragement and hopelessness.

Feelings of disconnection from God, isolation, and shattering of spiritual beliefs may cause a missionary to withdraw from social support at the very time it is most needed. If you are experiencing spiritual confusion, remember that this is not unusual, and that many trauma survivors have successfully come through this time. Many find their spiritual views are deepened and clarified in the weeks and months that follow trauma. Talking with a trusted counselor or pastor about the confusion you are experiencing, praying for God's insight and comfort, and believing that the Lord will reveal his purpose over time are important.

What can I do to deal with spiritual confusion?

Factors that enable you to be resilient, to bounce back over time, and to work through your time of confusion include social support and good relationships, adaptability, optimism, flexibility, resourcefulness, and a tendency to look for meaning in the tragedy. Your ability to trust God through the difficult times when life is confusing, and your ability to hang on like Job during his time of tragedy, will be helpful. As you talk to spiritual counselors and allow yourself to grapple with difficult questions, you will find that your hope and faith are strengthened.

Remember to take care of yourself—body, mind, and spirit. Eat right, exercise, get enough rest, find a place to go for refreshment and accept offered encouragement. Allow yourself to cry and grieve. If you enjoy journaling and writing, take time to record your thoughts and feelings. Listen to calming music, and learn relaxation techniques such as slow breathing. As you read scripture, ask the Lord to guide your thoughts and to help you with your struggles. Try to be patient with yourself. Others have struggled with these difficult questions and are willing to listen, pray for you, and encourage you. In time you will find healing and strength. Holding the hand of someone who may have walked in your shoes can make a world of difference as you suffer.

Remember, as you allow someone to help you in your time of spiritual darkness, they may be blessed and grow while reaching out to you.

Substance Abuse

As an MK living near Colombia, I found that drugs were easily available to me on every street corner. Drinking was not illegal, and so I began drinking covertly with the nationals in middle school. Some of my friends and I began smoking marijuana, and then gradually moved into trying harder drugs. I was a heavy user by the time I was eighteen.

What is substance abuse?

Substance abuse is the excessive use of alcohol, polysubstances, or prescription drugs. The substance of abuse could be food, marijuana, prescription and non-prescription drugs, caffeine, alcohol, or nicotine. Sometimes abuse leads to addiction. Addiction requires treatment for sustained recovery to occur, because relapse is common. There are many choices for treatment, but the key is diagnosis, education, support, and treatment.

Missionaries and family members may use a substance because it brings feelings of pleasure, or because it overcomes physical pain from an injury. Some substances lead to escape and some drugs cover uncomfortable feelings—temporarily. The brain responds differently depending on the substance of abuse. Some believe one can become addicted to sex as well, including pornography. This may be a means of escape, power, and an effort to hide pain or find companionship when the missionary suffers from trauma or unsatisfying relationships in some aspect of life.

Substance abuse is devastating to your spiritual life and to ministry. The person under the control of substances no longer relies on God's power to overcome problems, but looks, at times unknowingly, to the substance to bring comfort. Consequences of substance abuse include difficulties with finances, destruction of health, destroyed relationships, and poor job performance. A person addicted to a substance often denies the truth, and learns to manipulate when needs are not met. Eventually dishonesty permeates the life of a substance abuser.

As substance use continues into abuse, tolerance grows to the substance so that more is required to achieve the desired effect. Life begins to fall apart. It may appear to be a race to see what you lose first—your family, friends, ministry, faith or your physical health. Those who suspect a friend or family member is abusing substances may notice changes in mood, sleep, blood pressure, irritability, hunger, weight, anger, and sexual functioning.

What can I do to begin my recovery from substance abuse?

The road to recovery is difficult, but entirely possible and more so with God's power. Take the first step. Admit to yourself and to others that something in your life is out of control. Honesty, confession, and accountability open the gate to recovery.

Some are able to stop using substances with God's help and strength after they make that first decision to quit. Most require the support of a program such as Alcoholics Anonymous because the power of addiction is extremely strong. Overcoming an addiction may require that you leave the mission field for a period of time to focus on breaking free. A counselor can help guide you, and there are many resources listed on the internet and in this book. Your family will need support too.

The value of Alcoholics Anonymous (AA) and Narcotics Anonymous (NA) is that not only does the abuser receive help and support, but the organizations refer to associated programs for the family and for those who care about you. Overeaters Anonymous (OA) is also an effective support group for individuals with food issues. These support groups observe a code of confidentiality and acceptance. Some churches and Christian counseling centers offer support groups for believers based on the principles of AA. If you are on leave in the United States, Canada, or the United Kingdom you may find meetings occurring regularly in most towns, giving you choices and regular assistance. They offer peer support and are "open" year-round. Many programs encourage someone battling an addiction to enroll in a treatment program while also attending a program such as AA.

Once you make the choice for treatment, you will need to learn what triggers the cravings for the substance you are using. You may discover unknown feelings behind your substance abuse history. Missionaries suffering symptoms of post-trauma may have been seeking to self-medicate their painful symptoms, and have become addicted unknowingly. This is all the more reason to seek treatment. Your counselors and peers at a support group will help you learn to avoid situations that lead to anxiety, fear, and stressors that may precipitate substance use.

Those who recover from substance abuse are eternally grateful to God for allowing them to get their lives back. A new life of spiritual wholeness awaits you, with improved health and the healing relationships. Please do not be ashamed to seek treatment.

Suicidal Thoughts/ideation

My friend Sherry was depressed for years, but nobody took her seriously when she made statements like, "I feel like dying." Distraught over family problems with her brothers, and feeling like an outcast at the missionary school, Sherry had periods of irrational thinking. She eventually came to believe that her death was God's will, and that God wanted her to die to bring her brothers closer to him. Sherry's suicide rocked the missionary community. I was wracked with guilt for not listening and realizing her suicide threats were genuine.

What are suicidal thoughts?
When a missionary or MK is experiencing depression, deep sadness, or perhaps even psychosis there may be a point when thoughts occur about ending life on this earth, and going to heaven where "there will be no more death or mourning or crying or pain." (Rev. 21:4) The thoughts begin to formulate, take shape, and may become repetitive. "Suicidal ideation" is a term that means thoughts of suicide, with or without a specific plan. These

thoughts range from a vague hopelessness of wanting to go away or sleep forever, to wanting to die. Suicidal ideation must be taken seriously the first time, and treated immediately.

If suicidal ideation (SI) is secondary to trauma, correct diagnosis is, again, critical so intervention and support can be provided. Prescription medication may be helpful for treating the mood, which most often precipitates suicidal thoughts. A brief hospitalization may be the safest choice when someone is feeling unsafe. SI may recur during anniversary times, after a time of loss, when experiencing chronic pain, or during other times of severe stress.

Suicidal behavior is when an individual acts on suicidal ideation. The level of a suicide attempt may be very dangerous, lethal, or a cry for help. Unfortunately, sometimes, such a cry goes unnoticed.

What can I do to safely cope with suicidal thoughts and behaviors?

If you harm yourself in *any* way, you need to seek help. Psychotherapy can shed insight into what led to the painful thoughts behind the action. Some type of treatment is essential. There is a great deal of fear for the family and missionary. It will take time for everyone to heal and regain trust.

If you are having difficulty coping with suicidal thoughts, write a safety plan and keep it in place for times when you may not feel strong. The safety plan should include names and numbers you can call at the first sign of suicidal ideation. Share this information with your family or those with whom you are closest. Clinical professionals can teach you how write a safety plan, and there is a sample in the back of this book. Basic information needed for the safety plan includes numbers of supporters in your life, your prescribers, family, and other important contact information.

It is important to make your home safe by not having access to guns or extra medication if you are very depressed and likely to experience suicidal thoughts.

It may be wise to keep your medication with a trusted person and only keep a day or week's worth of medication at a time in your home. Work this out with one of your providers in a realistic conversation knowing your safety and long-term health is the goal. It is never worth taking a risk with your safety and always important to remember, "Better safe than sorry."

When you begin treatment, you will learn to identify triggers to suicidal ideation. You will learn to talk about your feelings. Preparation is important and will lessen the fear, anxiety, and panic associated with ideas of suicide. Developing problem-solving skills will help you to think about the future.

A Christian counselor will help you search to find God's meaning and purpose for your life. How do you matter in the body of Christ? What are your reasonable goals? Have you thought about your spiritual health? One day at a time you will learn to feel safe again. Confidence in the Lord and in self will return and grow. Positive coping skills will work for you. Support from others will make the road easier and less lonely. Remember the resources in the back of this book. The websites, phone numbers, books and articles are listed for you. Learning to think safely when you have dark thoughts is a process. With help, support and education from trained professionals who care, you can move forward and past the darkness.

Safety Plan

One of the most important actions for anyone to take along their treatment path is to write a safety plan. This plan will serve as a guide if you begin to feel unsafe and to remind you of safe names and numbers to call in the case of a crisis. A safety plan is a personal written document, which can be formal or informal. The important thing is that the plan includes familiar, helpful, real, practical, comfortable and updated information that is readily at hand should the missionary or family member have need of it. From listed coping skills to negative triggers, a safety plan is a "roadmap" to keep available should there be a time of confusion, frustration, panic, loneliness or feeling of danger.

This information will be most helpful if copied and kept in several places because a crisis can happen at any time. It is best to let several people know about a safety plan. The treatment team will help formulate a safety plan, or, if you are reading this book you can write a safety plan using the ideas below.

It may be convenient to put this information on an index card. Photocopy your plan and keep a copy in a place where it is easily found in your home, and then give a copy to a close friend and keep another copy on or close to you.

Remember to write a "contract" within the safety plan. This is a personal promise agreeing, with honor, not to cause self-harm (or harm to someone else).

Contract for Safety

Name_____

Date of Birth_____

Name of Psychiatric Provider_____

Phone Number_____

Name of psychotherapist_____

Phone Number_____

Name of Medical Provider_____

Phone Number_____

Crisis Hotline_____

Second Crisis Hotline_____

Good Friend Name_____

Phone Number_____

Sponsor (Alcoholics Anonymous, Narcotics Anonymous, Overeaters
Anonymous whatever may be appropriate)_____

Phone Number_____

Names and numbers to call_____

Diagnostic information_____

Triggers to relapse_____

Positive coping skills to remember_____

Allergies_____

Safe places_____

Appendix 1:
Commonly Asked Questions

I'm a Christian missionary, and I've been wondering what the difference is between mental health problems and spiritual problems. How can I tell them apart?

Many believers, not just missionaries, struggle with this question. If I have feelings of anger, fear, worry, or depression, is that just a lack of faith? Shouldn't my understanding of scripture and my personal walk with God be enough to take care of these problems and make the feelings go away?

In the last fifty years, the fields of psychology and psychiatry have grown enormously. Studies of the brain show us that anxiety and depression, as well as great happiness, precipitate chemical changes in the brain. God designed our bodies and minds to interact together in the most amazing way so our emotions are natural expressions of the circumstances we face. When we are upset, our faith in God and our spiritual thoughts help us manage powerful emotions. Sometimes these emotions are so overwhelming they require further assistance.

Just the way medical doctors treat broken bones and internal diseases by providing medication, surgery, and interventions for healing, psychiatric providers are successfully treating anxiety disorders and other mental health diagnoses with medication and various interventions.

You would probably go to a medical doctor for your physical ailments without worrying about whether this showed a lack of faith in God. In the same way, missionaries may go to psychologists, psychiatrists, psychiatric nurse practitioners, and various licensed counselors who will offer education and provide a wide array of therapies for mental health problems.

Spiritual and mental health problems are often woven so closely together that separating one from another becomes difficult. Acknowledging the need for help is the key to moving forward. Finding someone with whom you feel comfortable is another important step in the process. Depending on where you live and your personal journey, you may end up feeling more comfortable with someone outside your circle of influence. There are many individuals of personal faith at work around the world. Word of mouth, as well as internet resources can lead you to their office door and a rewarding therapeutic relationship.

Christian professionals believe that a person's spiritual life is an important part of healing, and often integrate their knowledge of Christ's teachings and theology to challenge faulty thinking as part of the intervention process. Prayer, meditation, scripture reading, and other spiritual disciplines may be included along with practical life and coping skills for anxiety, depression, and other concerns.

Mental health problems are described in the treatment manual called *The Diagnostic and Statistical Manual of Mental Disorders, TR-IV (DSM TR-IV)*. Believers share the same emotional symptoms as non-believers. We are all human beings living in this world. May we all be open to his healing grace.

It is our hope and sincere prayer that the information within these pages will be helpful to you, answer questions, and empower you to seek more answers if you still have them. We hope it will lead you to resources specific to your needs, be they medical, spiritual, or psychological. Your pain may come from unexpected places. This is not uncommon, but can be surprising to someone who has not experienced trauma before. It may be difficult to reach out to someone for support when you are used to being strong and in charge. Remember, one step at a time. Healing is possible for you. This is the beginning, and there is help available, sometimes closer than you think. You are reading this book for a reason. Keep reading...

> *I am a missionary who has been through a difficult and traumatic experience. I am ashamed to say that my spiritual beliefs have suffered as a result. I keep asking God what in the world was he thinking to let these terrible events happen on the field. I no longer feel like a strong Christian leader. Is it possible that I have missed God's direction and call?*

Traumatic events experienced by missionaries can cause them to question their calling and the spiritual beliefs they once held as true. (Please see our section on Spiritual confusion.) Doubt, discouragement, and spiritual questions are very common for those who experience tragedy and trauma.

A supportive counselor will help you talk through the questions that are troubling you, and will help you process your sadness, grief and loss. Many missionaries have found that their time of discouragement was productive and life-changing, because God used the time of suffering to bring a new depth of understanding. Your ideas about life and ministry may change during this period of time, and you may be surprised to see how the Lord strengthens and guides you in new ways.

We hope the information in this book will help you in your recovery. You will find information about caring for the whole person—body, mind, and spirit. As you read scripture, ask the Lord to guide your thoughts and to help you with your struggles. Be patient with yourself. Talk to others who have struggled with these difficult questions. Let them pray for you, listen, and encourage you. In time you will find healing and strength.

I'm not a missionary, but I support missionaries financially, pray for them, and host them while they're in the homeland. I've noticed that some missionaries change dramatically after a term on the field, and don't connect with us in the same way as before. How can this book help?

It is difficult to imagine the world of the missionary if you have not lived it. Missionary life is rewarding, challenging, and sometimes defeating. Not for the faint of heart, missionary work draws the bravest and best to respond to the call of God on their lives. Missionaries are a hearty stock—innovative, intelligent, practical, self-sacrificing, optimistic, and above all spiritually dedicated to a cause. The mission may be their life's work and ultimate accomplishment. Many do not or cannot talk about the negative aspects because it is too difficult for them to do so.

Missionaries serve in virtually every country in the world; some openly, some quietly or covertly. Missionaries may live in danger. Their objective is both humanitarian and spiritual. They fight against poverty, war, and sickness; they educate the people and work to improve the economy, often providing goods and services for people in nations with few resources. Missionaries spread the Good News, at times suffering criticism for attempting to implement change within a culture. Sometimes they are accused of taking advantage of vulnerable communities devastated by poverty, war, and corruption. Missionaries learn early on that everyone will not appreciate their hard work and sacrifices. Some will dismiss their spiritual calling. Even so, many continue to hear the voice of the Lord, give up all they own, and walk away from a safe, comfortable, and seemingly "normal" life. In doing so, they may risk the security of their families to serve in remote, impoverished, and often dangerous places.

Missionaries have the same strengths as all people and, because we are all fully human, the same weaknesses. Mission organizations have enormously improved in the past two decades, often carefully screening their candidates for authenticity of faith, emotional stability, social skills, and the ability to withstand stress. The sending organization may attempt to reassign those who are not able to withstand the pressures of missionary service. The goal is certainly for all those who go into missionary service to experience success. As much as possible, missionaries are prepared in advance for the culture into which they will go. They are taught the language, encouraged to create a support network, and do their best to establish the necessary resources for successful cultural integration.

Even so, unforeseen traumatic events may occur. Not only that, some missionaries choose to remain in dangerous settings to continue the work to which they feel called. Shocking, life-threatening experiences may lead to stress reactions, which can be debilitating to the best of missionaries. It is important to draw on spiritual disciplines and walk with God to assist you through times of crisis. Faith in the Lord has carried many a missionary through the darkest of nights. It is true that time may help with healing when someone has experienced trauma. Remember, every individual is unique in his or her response to trauma.

Denial of symptoms is common among strong, independent, and confident leaders. Often, it is the heart's desire of a missionary to talk about God's protection, glory, and purpose when there is a tragedy. There may also be subtle, or not so subtle, pressure on the missionary to not mention the emotional or physical problems that occur in the aftermath of trauma. Friends of the missionary may recognize personality changes, signs, or symptoms the missionary does not recognize. Supporters may not know how to address this while respecting the missionary's privacy. Accepting feedback or listening when someone says something about a noted mood change after a trauma is a good first step. Keep praying for your missionary friends, and love and support them. Direct them to a counselor if the Lord shows you to do this. Pray for an opportunity, an open door, to offer support. Hand them this book, offer them a name of a confidential counselor, or just let them know you are there for them when they are ready to talk.

Appendix 2:
Confidence Builders:
Positive Self-talk From Scripture

The precepts of the Lord are right, giving joy to the heart. The commands of the Lord are radiant, giving light to the eyes. - Ps. 19:8

If you are experiencing any of the signs or symptoms in this book, you may have a negative internal voice speaking to you. That voice may be hard to recognize if you do not take the time to listen, but it is your internal dialogue—the quiet things you say to yourself, for better or worse that can make a big difference in your life. During times of crisis, the voice of fear and disillusionment may overwhelm good judgment. A negative inner dialogue may be at the core of anxiety and depression. This is called "negative self-talk."

The Bible tells us that God's word, the precepts of the Lord bring joy to the heart and give light to the eyes. Joy speaks of happiness, and renewed peace; light symbolizes vision, insight, direction, and guidance for whatever frightening situation one may face. God's word is positive self-talk to be stored in your mind, savored, digested, and built into your soul. The word will then be in your heart during the storms of life so you do not lose your inner strength, but are able to fight against fear, terror, discouragement, hopelessness, and depression.

Below are nine principles, along with verses from scripture, that will help you rebuild your confidence. Take the time to learn the verses, to speak them, and to allow God's words of truth to change the voice of fear inside. As Romans 12:2 says, *"Be transformed by the renewing of your mind."*

1.   God loves me and always will, no matter what

I have loved you with an everlasting love; I have drawn you with loving-kindness. Jer. 31:3b

Who shall separate us from the love of Christ? Shall trouble or hardship or persecution or famine or nakedness or danger or sword?....No, in all these things we are more than conquerors through him who loved us. For I am convinced that neither death nor life, neither angels nor demons, neither the present nor the future, nor any powers, neither height nor depth, nor anything else in all creation, will be able to separate us from the love of God that is in Christ Jesus our Lord. Rom. 8:35-39

Because of the Lord's great love we are not consumed, for his compassions never fail. They are new every morning; great is your faithfulness. Lam. 3:22-23

2.   God is my strength and my helper

The Lord is my light and my salvation—whom shall I fear? The Lord is the stronghold of my life—of whom shall I be afraid? Ps. 27:1

God is our refuge and strength, an ever-present help in trouble. Ps. 46:1

When I am afraid, I will trust in you. Ps. 56:3

I will lie down and sleep in peace, for you alone, O Lord, make me dwell in safety. Ps. 4:8

3.   God answers me when I call

When I called, you answered me; you made me bold and stouthearted. Ps. 138:3

This is what the Lord says, he who made the earth, the Lord who formed it and established it—the Lord is his name: 'Call to me and I will answer you and tell you great and unsearchable things you do not know.' Jer. 33:2-3

I call to the Lord, who is worthy of praise, and I am saved from my enemies. Ps. 18:3

Call upon me in the day of trouble; I will deliver you, and you will honor me. Ps. 50:15

4. **With God's help I have what I need to succeed**

I have learned the secret of being content in any and every situation, whether well fed or hungry, whether living in plenty or in want. I can do everything through him who gives me strength. Phil. 4:12b-13

And my God will meet all your needs according to his glorious riches in Christ Jesus. Phil. 4:19

Even youths grow tired and weary, and young men stumble and fall; but those who hope in the Lord will renew their strength. They will soar on wings like eagles; they will run and not grow weary, they will walk and not be faint. Isa. 40:30-31

5. **There is something special and unique about me**

You created my inmost being; you knit me together in my mother's womb. I praise you because I am fearfully and wonderfully made; your works are wonderful, I know that full well. Ps. 139:13-14

The Lord does not look at the things man looks at. Man looks at the outward appearance, but the Lord looks at the heart. 1 Sam. 16:7b

6. **My strengths and weaknesses are helped by others**

But in fact God has arranged the parts of the body, every one of them, just as he wanted them to be....those parts of the body that seem to be weaker are indispensable, and the parts that we think are less honorable we treat with special honor....so that there should be no division in the body, but that its parts should have equal concern for each other. If one part suffers, every part suffers with it; if one part is honored, every part rejoices with it. Now you are the body of Christ, and each one of you is a part of it. 1 Cor. 12:18, 22-23, 25-27

We have different gifts; according to the grace given us....share with God's people who are in need. Rom. 12:6, 13

7. **God has good plans for my life**

"For I know the plans I have for you," declares the Lord, "Plans to prosper you and not harm you, plans to give you hope and a future." Jer. 29:11

Surely goodness and love will follow me all the days of my life, and I will dwell in the house of the Lord forever. Ps. 23:6

8.   **When bad things happen, God works through them for good**

And we know that in all things God works for the good of those who love him, who have been called according to his purpose....If God is for us, who can be against us? He who did not spare his own son, but gave him up for us all—how will he not also, along with him, graciously give us all things? Rom. 8:28, 31b-32

And the God of all grace, who called you to his eternal glory in Christ, after you have suffered a little while, will himself restore you and make you strong, firm, and steadfast. 1 Pet. 5:10

Dear friends, do not be surprised at the painful trial you are suffering, as though something strange were happening to you. But rejoice that you participate in the sufferings of Christ, so that you may be overjoyed when his glory is revealed....So then, those who suffer according to God's will should commit themselves to their faithful Creator and continue to do good. 1 Pet. 4:12, 19

Praise be to the God and Father of our Lord Jesus Christ, the Father of compassion and the God of all comfort, who comforts us in all our troubles, so that we can comfort those in any trouble with the comfort we ourselves have received from God. For just as the sufferings of Christ flow over into our lives, so also through Christ our comfort overflows... which produces in you patient endurance of the same sufferings we suffer. 2 Cor. 1:3-6

9.   **I am focusing on the good things in my life**

Whatever is true, whatever is noble, whatever is right, whatever is pure, whatever is lovely, whatever is admirable—if anything is excellent or praiseworthy—think about such things...and the God of peace will be with you. Phil. 4:8-9

We also rejoice in our sufferings, because we know that suffering produces perseverance; perseverance, character; and character, hope. And hope does not disappoint us, because God has poured out his love into our hearts by the Holy Spirit, whom he has given us. Rom. 5:3-5

Appendix 3:
Diagnostic And Statistical Manual Of Mental Disorders For Post-traumatic Stress Disorder

A. The person has been exposed to a traumatic event in which both of the following were present:

1. the person experienced, witnessed, or was confronted with an event or events that involved actual or threatened death or serious injury, or a threat to the physical integrity of self or others
2. the person's response involved intense fear, helplessness, or horror

B. The traumatic event is persistently re-experienced in one (or more) of the following ways:

1. recurrent and intrusive distressing recollections of the event, including images, thoughts, or perceptions
2. recurrent distressing dreams of the event
3. acting or feeling as if the traumatic event were recurring (includes a sense of reliving the experience, illusions, hallucinations, and dissociative flashback episodes, including those that occur on awakening or when intoxicated)
4. intense psychological distress at exposure to internal or external

cues that symbolize or resemble an aspect of the traumatic event

5. physiological reactivity on exposure to internal or external cues that symbolize or resemble an aspect of the traumatic event

C. Persistent avoidance of stimuli associated with the trauma and numbing of general responsiveness (not present before the trauma), as indicated by three (or more) of the following:

1. efforts to avoid thoughts, feelings, or conversations associated with the trauma
2. efforts to avoid activities, places, or people that arouse recollections of the trauma
3. inability to recall an important aspect of the trauma
4. markedly diminished interest or participation in significant activities
5. feeling of detachment or estrangement from others
6. restricted range of affect (e.g., unable to have loving feelings)
7. sense of a foreshortened future (e.g., does not expect to have a career, marriage, children, or normal life span)

D. Persistent symptoms of increased arousal (not present before the trauma), as indicated by two (or more) of the following:

1. difficulty falling or staying asleep
2. irritability or outbursts of anger
3. difficulty concentrating
4. hyper-vigilance
5. exaggerated startle response

E. Duration of the disturbance (symptoms in criteria B, C, and D) is more than one month

F. The disturbance causes clinically significant distress or impairment in social, occupational, or other important areas of functioning

Specify if:
    Acute: if duration of symptoms is less than three months.
    Chronic: if duration of symptoms is three months or more.
Specify if:
    With delayed onset: If onset of symptoms is at least six months after the stressor.

Appendix 4:
Missionaries And
Families' Writings

All the stories included are the recollections of missionaries who experienced traumatic events while on the mission field. If they wish to be identified, their real names are included. Others asked to remain anonymous, and their identities are protected by changing their names and some of the identifying locations or circumstances.

A Sea-side Tragedy

My husband David and I arrived in Ecuador in August of 1959 as missionaries with a Short Wave Radio Facility and Medical Mission known as HCJB. David taught in the school for missionary children. Our students, children of Protestant missionaries serving in Ecuador and other countries in South America, either lived with their parents in Quito or in dorms. We also served a community of expatriates whose children were our students. Each year, the graduating class went on a special retreat to the ocean as a final gathering before leaving Ecuador.

In 1968 we drove from Quito on a ten-hour trip to Salinas, a fishing community set on the edge of the Pacific Ocean. David and I had the sole responsibility for supervising twenty-three graduating students on this senior class retreat. Our two-year-old daughter was also with us.

On an isolated beach on the coast of Ecuador known as Mar Bravo (Wild Sea), one of our students was swept out to sea and drowned. My husband, a strong swimmer, was unable to save Jimmy Roberson, the youngest member of the graduating class and the smallest of all the young people. Jimmy's parents were missionary colleagues and our next door neighbors in Quito. Jimmy's loss, the futile search for his body, the arrival of his parents the next morning, the responsibility of supporting his classmates, the eventual return to Quito, and the memorial service within our missionary community are memories that remain today as deep wounds of sorrow for the day we lost this young man, a student who was literally torn from my husband's grasp and washed into eternity.

The emotional symptoms we experienced were far greater than our physical inability to sleep. While deeply sorrowful, we had to continue to be present for the twenty-two young people still under our care, so we had to step back from our own grief and provide a safe place for the expression of their sorrow.

We felt enormous fear when the students voted to remain in Salinas for the rest of their retreat and wanted to go to a safer beach the day following the drowning. Our desire was to remain with the students, for this was a shared trauma and none of us wanted to go back into the Andes until Jimmy had been found. Eventually we all realized there would be no body, although helicopter search teams arrived from Panama. Other missionaries arrived to support us, but we stayed with the students.

We felt tremendous guilt and shame. Guilt meant taking responsibility for what transpired. Shame meant facing Jimmy's parents at water's edge, and that shame continued when we returned to our Quito community.

Although Jimmy's parents expressed to us, over and over again and in multiple ways, that we were not responsible for their son's death, we could not let go of the weight of that overwhelming responsibility. Jimmy's parents were even able to tell us they were "happy" that David had not drowned as he battled the waves while trying to reach Jimmy. To this day we embrace the fact that caring for others means bearing a responsibility to protect them, and in this instance, we were unable to do so.

The memorial service for Jimmy in the school gym did a great deal to comfort David. However, he found it extremely difficult to be with others. He imagined they didn't know what to say to him and therefore were ignoring him, or saying things to him which did not offer comfort. In reality, our missionary community never publicly voiced any negative comments or sense of disappointment over what transpired during that terrible day.

Jimmy drowned on March 7, 1968. The memories from that morning are as immediate and fresh in our spirits as if it all had happened a few months ago. This was the first traumatic event in our marriage, and we were in our early thirties. I have never ventured into the ocean again to swim, except when staying close to the shore in a placid sea. There has never been a time that we have not kept a close eye on our own family and the children of others when they have been in the surf.

A letter from one of our missionary doctors is something we cherish to this day. In the letter, so important to us, this kind man wrote of his own tragic experience. He had encouraged a tribal family to allow him to operate on the deformed hand of their young son. This simple procedure would give the child back the use of his hand and allow him to live in the jungles without limitations. During the surgery, the child had died. His letter read, "David and Kay, we must live with the risks and never draw back from doing good."

- Rev. Kay Landers
Kay is a wife, mother, grandmother, and a retired missionary who presently serves as a chaplain.

Dealing With Depression On The Mission Field

My husband, children and I were serving in Africa as young missionaries, and during this time we experienced a series of traumatic incidents.

One day I suffered a monkey bite. At first I went to an African clinic to be treated where I was sewn up with no pain killer. I went into shock and was then sent to an American doctor who treated me, but I suffered a drug reaction and an infection. The bite took about two or three months to heal and left me emotionally shaken.

Shortly after this, my daughter went to a boarding school in another country while we remained in our place of service. Along with the normal loneliness, tears, and sense of loss, the separation became more difficult by the boarding school's policy that discouraged parents from calling their children. Each time we called to talk to them, my husband and I were tearful. I felt depressed, lonely, and nearly immobilized.

Two strong Christian women supported me during this time with love and encouragement. I experienced severe depression. Because I didn't try to hide my condition, others were wonderful to me, especially my husband and our director. Finally I visited a psychiatrist who prescribed medication, and I got better. I eventually returned to Africa and learned to cope.

We have moved twenty times in our years of service. I have had my depression under control since 1990, but occasionally it returns. Now, when it returns, I know what to do.

-Norma

Coping With Instability And Violence

During the latter part of the 1990's, my wife and I served in a third-world country that was in the midst of a prolonged civil war. The security situation was so perilous that family members could not remain in the country, so I found myself separated from my wife and kids, on a different continent, for a total of eighteen months. True to prediction, our mission hospital got caught up in the fighting. Over the course of several months we were 'visited' by rebel soldiers and other armed elements; we were robbed of our supplies, our personnel were attacked; and one of our national doctors was killed. We remained a staff of eighty persons trying to keep a four hundred bed hospital open in the midst of war, cut off from the capital city with dwindling supplies, resources and resolve.

I was the medical director at the time and many looked to me for the answers. I felt that I had failed miserably. Once in the heat of the conflict, I was escorted away by rebel soldiers, questioned, threatened, and intimidated, but never harmed. I remember almost welcoming the intimidation, in a strange way believing I deserved punishment for allowing tragedy and failure to befall the institution and personnel under my care.

I didn't recognize it at the time, but I was experiencing symptoms consistent with depression. I had no appetite and wasn't sleeping. Nighttime was an occasion to take long walks unseen by others and weep. If I had been my own physician, I would have given myself a psychological evaluation with a recommendation to evacuate…but then again we were cut off and had no way out.

Eventually, the war ended; the borders opened up and my mission board sent a small plane to get me. I remember that I was conflicted about leaving; I didn't want to leave our national staff and patients…but I desperately wanted to see my family. I cried on the long, 18-hour commercial flight home to the United States.

My wife and children greeted me at the airport. They looked so… wonderful! I traded in my raggedy clothes for real ones. I took a long, hot shower, sat in a real car, and ate incredibly well. I spent time with the family. Finally, the weight of the hospital was off my shoulders. I got to the place where I could spend a full day not thinking about the institution. My appetite returned as I slept a whole night through and I stopped taking walks alone. I even found my smile.

What I learned (several years after the fact) was that despite my beliefs to the contrary, at the time, I was never alone. God was with me each and every day, and through each trial. My error was that I relied too much on my own reliance, and not on God. I failed to realize that this was God's work and not mine….and by focusing on my own shortfalls and not God's provisions, I became depressed. Only when I came out of the situation (post-conflict) and saw how God kept the work going (we continued to receive and see over eight hundred people a day) did I find joy.

-Brian, a physician, father, and medical missionary.

A Missionary Kid's Experience Of Abuse

My parents were missionaries in a rural part of South America, and in third grade I was sent to boarding school for my education so both my parents could continue to work in the ministry. It was customary at that time to send MKs to a private Christian school run by a mission organization, and to house them in dorms with a house parent selected by the mission. Children were encouraged to hide their homesickness, because they were told the Lord's work was so important they didn't want to hinder their parents' work by showing neediness. Most of the missionary parents had no idea what real dorm life was like, and most of us didn't tell them.

I was sexually, emotionally, physically, and spiritually abused by both house parents in the dorm where I lived. The dorm father raped me, and sometimes the dorm mother would join in. I would be taken from my dorm room, my classroom, and even my Sunday School room. The dorm father demonstrated to me how he would kill me or my sister if I told anyone. The abuse continued for two years, ending only when the house parents suddenly left the field. Later I learned that other girls were also abused by these house parents.

Throughout my life I've experienced disconnected moments. I've looked into the mirror and not recognized the face looking back at me at all. I've had the feeling of viewing a flashback action and moment from above and not actually being part of it—just "floating" around it. There have been many anxiety attacks, irrational fears, and times of feeling paralyzed physically and emotionally. I've had suicidal and violent thoughts. I've been super-vigilant when it comes to my children and family.

For years I was the "invisible" person and didn't know how to handle it when people remembered me from South America. I've had recurrent nightmares, lots of sleeping problems, and eating disorders—both binge eating and not eating at all. I've had body twitches and have gone through a time when my fists clenched up so tightly, that even my husband had trouble helping me open them. My skin has broken out in pimples and hives. My relationships have suffered, too. What is love? Can I really allow myself to feel things emotionally?

I finally started counseling when I was thirty-five. It was a long haul and very hard to do, but I knew it had to be done. I can now, usually, look at things differently. I've been able to let go of some of the guilt and shame.

I have accepted that PTSD symptoms are part of who I am. I am still, and always will be, a work in progress. Things pop up out of the blue that will take my breath away, and it'll take me awhile to feel like I can breathe normally again. The difference is that now, the impact is not as debilitating as it once was, and I know that things will get better and I can get through this—even if it feels like I can't. My symptoms are still there and may always be, just not to the degree they once were.

-Cathy. Today Cathy is a school teacher, a wife and mother of two. She struggles bravely against her symptoms and hopes her story will help someone else.

Multiple Tragedies And Burn-out

While we were missionaries in Africa we went through a wave of incidents, in a four to five month period, so that we hadn't really recovered from one incident before another hit us. Our struggles began when we moved from one ministry location to another as we were taking over leadership of a group of new missionaries. We felt God leading us, but it was very hard to leave friends and "family" in the other location.

Shortly thereafter, we were coming back from vacation with some of our teammates, and on the way I rolled our Land Rover. The vehicle was totaled, we were shaken, and my one-year-old was thrown thirty to forty feet from the car. He broke his leg in two places and fractured his head. After recovering from this, we had another accident where I ran over three sheep in the road. We made it to where we were headed and two days later had a break-in by a gang of thieves. They hit me over the head with a machete and tried to enter our bedroom where my wife and son were hiding. Our mission asked us to go to a care center in the next country for debriefing, and during this time we discovered my wife was in need of major surgery for uterine tumors.

We both felt burnt-out afterwards, and yet we had a team to continue to lead for another year. At the end of the term I was totally spent. I didn't want to be around people. I had trouble engaging, even my family. We adopted our second child around this time, but I had no energy to give. I continually felt tired for our whole furlough and even into our next term of service. I had feelings of despair, depression, regret, and unworthiness.

That was five years ago. I received rest and a decreased work load for a while. I still have a slight pressure above the eyes, which requires me to wear non-prescription glasses to shield them from the glare. Otherwise, I feel much more energetic and better able to enter into relationships again than I have for a long time.

-Scott. Scott and his wife have been missionaries in East Africa for 10 years. They have 3 boys, ages 2, 3, and 6 at the time they wrote their story.

Fear And Anxiety

We were serving as missionaries in Asia in the mid-1990's, and at the time my sons were four- and five-years-old. One day we were waiting at a train station, standing at the end of the platform. A person in the middle section of the ramp committed suicide as we were standing there. He stepped deliberately off the platform in front of the incoming train. Thankfully, we were too far down to see details. I tried my best to shield the boys, but we were stuck there at the train station for about thirty minutes.

My younger son did not see or understand this, but was traumatized by the screech of the train wheels, the shrill whistle, and the smoke from the brakes. For some time he startled at the sound of train whistles. I kept seeing images in my mind of the person on the tracks and the following events. I had great difficulty concentrating enough to make dinner that night. I continued replaying the scene and the sounds, along with my words and actions.

My older son saw the person jump and was most affected. Usually talkative, he had a hard time discussing it. After a week he became upset with me for not getting the boys out of there and for not witnessing to that person to prevent the suicide.

My older son and I experienced great distress in train stations. We weren't afraid of the trains; we felt we couldn't trust people to stay on the platform. We spent over a year working through this fear. We'd hold hands at the very end of the platform and only watch our approaching train. Gradually we moved down a space or two so that a small group was between us and the coming train. We never again could comfortably watch a train approach from the other direction in front of a sea of people. My husband dealt with guilt at not being able to protect his family, and frustration at not being able to fully identify with our experience or reactions.

We sought help from our mission board and from the library of the missionary school. No help was available. We encouraged the mission board and school to make a trauma resource available to the whole mission community. Weeks later school kids witnessed a similar trauma and several parents contacted us for advice in helping their children.

We are based in the U.S. now, but I think I'd still experience some anxiety on a train or subway platform. My older son recently has been reprocessing this trauma and has had a few dreams related to the event. His memory of that time, so long ago, also includes bloody details that he either filled in over the years, I blocked out, or never saw. It seems he has needed to understand, as an older teen, what he could never grasp as a child. He knows I could not have stopped what happened or done anything much different in protecting him, but he still feels that he must share a degree of guilt as well as sadness over the event. He also thinks it caused him to think about death and dying more deeply and frequently than other kids of that age, when it occurred.

-Allison, a former missionary in Asia, wife and mother

Witnessing A Tragic Death

We were serving as missionaries in eastern Africa. On the weekend of our third wedding anniversary, my wife Mary and I piled into our 4-Runner with our young daughter Cathy and headed north to a Game Reserve. We spent several days up there enjoying the animals, relaxing, and getting away from the city.

On our way home the following week, we took a longer, more scenic route. It was an area that we hadn't seen yet. About a half a mile past a routine traffic police checkpoint, an eighteen-year-old Muslim man, who was looking right at us, stepped in front of our truck. By the time I realized he wasn't planning on getting out of the way, it was too late for me to swerve, so I slammed on the brakes. Our 4-Runner hit him while skidding to a stop. The man was suddenly "draped" over the front of our truck. When the car fully stopped, the man rolled off the hood and onto the road in front of us. He did not move again.

I immediately jumped out and ran to help him, but saw that he had died instantly. A small truck had been traveling in the opposite direction, and when the driver stopped to see what had happened, I yelled for him to return to the traffic police stop to get a cop down there right away.

By this time a crowd had formed. They yelled at me to take the dead man to the major town just a few miles away. Within minutes, a police officer was on the scene. He marked off the pavement where the truck had stopped and the body lay, and then agreed that we should take the body to the hospital. I remember the crowd getting more and more angry and restless, so the policeman had urged us to leave.

Meanwhile, Mary was in the car with the doors locked and the tinted windows up, calling our director to ask for help to come. Mary had crawled into the back seat to be with Cathy, who was completely oblivious to what was happening. The body of the Muslim man we hit was put into the front seat with someone to accompany it. The cop then jumped into the small bit of space remaining in our back seat. We headed into town.

At the hospital, the accident victim was officially pronounced dead. From there, we drove with the police officer to the police station and began all of the formalities, which included returning to the scene of the accident, taking measurements, speaking with people there, returning to the station again, and taking more initial statements. Our vehicle needed to be inspected, but since it was a Sunday afternoon, the truck was impounded until I could return the next morning. Michelle and I had to go back the next day and give our "official" statements. Then we went through the process of getting the vehicle repaired and waited nervously to see what the police would come up with in their investigation.

Immediately after the accident, we wrote a letter to our supporters, recounting God's protection during the incident. We wrote, "How do we find God's hand at work in the midst of a tragedy, especially if that tragedy involves you and a loss of life? …God is in control. He already knows the outcome. Please continue to pray for us emotionally and spiritually as we deal with this. Please pray for the family of the victim. They were Muslim and I don't know how they will take this. Please pray that the Lord will continue to show his handiwork in all of this and to use this for his glory."

After our traumatic event, Mary had all of the classic PTSD symptoms. Within ten months she ended up becoming very depressed, isolating herself, feeling angry, etc. One evening she and I sat down and tried to figure out where the depression had come from. We traced it all back to the very day of the accident, almost to the very hour. She had literally "shut" herself down that day, in order to protect our daughter from any anxiety. That is where she had been stuck, almost to the hour when Mary realized that she needed to be as "normal" as possible for Cathy.

We had a debriefing session with our mission's member care team within the first thirty-six hours. Our mission requires we debrief within forty-eight hours of an accident or incident. We are blessed to have a counseling center right here in our city, run by our mission. Mary and I had six or seven counseling sessions ten months later, and Mary found that she had forgotten some of the details of the incident, in particular some of the scarier parts about an official who was clearly angry and glaring at us with hatred for what he felt we had done. There had been fearful moments after the accident, when Mary wondered what would happen to them next. Since then, my wife has been afraid of driving, even in a city.

-Rex and Mary, missionaries in Africa

Children And Traumatic Stress

As a missionary kid at age seven, I remember being in our house in the Middle East, hidden under blankets in the safest room while an air-to-ground bombing was going on less than one mile from our house. At the time, my father was seriously ill with hepatitis, and my mother managed the kids by having us read "Snoopy." When there was a lull in the war, we were evacuated to the United States. Even once we were back in safety, I continued to be afraid of toilets flushing, airplanes flying overhead, and the lockers clanging in the halls of public school.

We were given lots of nurture and attention by the mission, but we were having symptoms that nobody recognized or addressed in third culture kids. I think the overt PTSD symptoms went away fairly quickly, due to the resilient nature of the brain, especially at that young age. However, the complicated issues of being a child in a war in the Middle East, with evangelical churches supporting us, took years to sort out. We had conflicting loyalties and were sent mixed messages. Sometimes I still have a hard time with July 4th fireworks and the sound of low-flying airplanes. I've learned how to overcome the mild anxiety I experience.

At this point, forty years later, I believe my experiences have pretty much been transformed into my ability to provide empathy and support to children in traumatic situations. For example, one of the most difficult things about the whole event was worrying about my father being left behind in the midst of a war while he was very, very ill, and my mother having to get us through the traumatic evacuation and re-entry into America. I realized, even as a child, that she was worried about my father, worried about us kids, our friends, the situation, and the church we left behind. During those years I think I tried very hard to not be a "problem" because, believe me, I knew my Mom had so much stress on her, and I was worried about her. Today, I think an important thing for children to know is that their parents are getting the help they need for everyone in the family.

-Lois Dvorak. Lois is a mother of three, wife, and clinical counselor who specializes in working with children and adolescents.

Accepting Help

While I was serving in Africa, a rebel group within our church began to cause problems with the people in the ministry. The situation escalated to the point that all of our small team was removed from the assignment and not allowed to return to the mission. I received death threats along with two other team mates.

Another time, we experienced a violent armed robbery at 2:30 a.m. on the compound where I lived. Masked men with guns cut the bars on the windows, entered the house, and demanded money. Fortunately, I was not harmed, although it was a gang attack and there were many gun shots fired. Later, I was indirectly involved with a volunteer and family who lived through a carjacking and shooting.

I have often felt spaced out, as if I have been on auto pilot. I have felt betrayed by the staff I worked with and trusted. Sometimes I felt like a failure. It seemed that I hadn't accomplished all that I should as a missionary. At times I have felt numb and unable to concentrate. I have become lethargic and depressed. I did not sleep well then, and sometimes had panic attacks. In the early days I was very jumpy at loud noises, especially at the sound of gunshots. I seemed to startle easily. The city in which I live is known for its crime. I sleep much better when I am able to get away from the city.

The mission supported me by providing intensive counseling. (I still check in with my provider every three to four months for my own well-being.) I took medication for depression for about eight to twelve months, and the other symptoms improved with ongoing sessions as needed. It was truly helpful. I am still aware of noises, but my adrenalin doesn't get going like before. Some of my symptoms have been healed with God's help, and some through help from others and by learning coping skills.

I know now when to seek help before things begin to even get out of hand. For me it has been a big learning curve to accept the help that is available. I am truly grateful for it and have learned much, which has enabled me to help others who have gone through similar experiences.

-Lisa. Lisa is a missionary from New Zealand, and has been serving in African missions for over 33 years.

Recovering From The Loneliness Of Depression

In 1980 we had been serving in Amman, Jordan, for nearly a year. I was nursing my infant son Caleb, and took him with me wherever I went. One day as I was driving to the Dead Sea, a man jumped in front of my car. Anxious to help him anyway they could, two of the car passengers put his body in the car and took him to a hospital. He was alive but badly injured— and within hours I was put in jail to protect me from the victim's family. I spent months in a Muslim court while we paid every penny we had for the man's hospital expenses. I had not been speeding or been irresponsible. Still, the driving laws in Jordan in 1980 were written to protect Bedouins. (I can still see his body going over the hood of our car when I think about that terrible day).

My husband was out of the country when this happened and could not be reached for security reasons. I had to depend on our Arab male staff to get me out of jail. I remember writing a list of all the ways that God had protected us during the time of the accident and its aftermath, but within weeks of the event, I came down with typhoid and our one-year-old son almost died of Shigella. Neither of us were able to regain our strength and become germ-free. For a number of months, we were considered "carriers" and couldn't be around the other staff. It was lonely.

I never received treatment, except for the typhoid, and our son was treated for his Shigella. Little Caleb and I finally had to return to the US for five weeks where we were treated further and were no longer carriers. It was the first time our families had seen Caleb since we had gone overseas when I was seven months pregnant.

When we returned to the US from the Middle East in 1987, I began going through severe clinical depression that didn't end until seven years later. I did go through counseling, but it wasn't as effective or helpful as I needed until I was placed on antidepressants long enough to really internalize the truth. I never stopped believing in God and his word, but I lost the capacity to experience it. It seemed like a big cosmic joke. After seven years of clinical depression marked by very poor sleep, constant anxiety, inability to eat, and severe weight loss, my brain was like a sieve...full of holes.

Friends intervened and took me to see a Christian counselor who gave me two weeks before talking with my husband about having me committed. Actually, dying seemed like a lovely option and I really thought my three kids would do better spiritually without me as such a lousy role model. Then, I again went on antidepressants, and after about six weeks on the meds, I began to realize that I once again had the capacity to choose how I felt and what my mind would be "set" on. I still needed to take God at his word, but I was able to comprehend and experience the truth of it again. I finally "got" grace. I was helpless to even cooperate with God as he took me from death back to life. So much of my performance-oriented hard-wiring died back there, but it all needed to die.

I have been on antidepressants since 1994 and my life wouldn't be worth living without them. I have been the human resources director of Trans World Radio for a number of years and I often say that I couldn't help our missionaries if my own family hadn't made so many mistakes. Lots of "traumatic" things happened. We lived through wars. We had no idea that a family of five shouldn't move as much as we did. We did many stupid things. Re-entry into the US was extremely difficult.

Clinical depression was so lonely. Now that God has brought me back to life, I am determined to talk about it and let fellow sufferers know that, looking back, it was the most spiritually-enriching period in my life. No question.

-Kris Carraway, is a former missionary in Jordan and HR director for Trans World Radio

Seeking God's Will And Protection

In 2002, our Mobile Member Care Team was on the campus of a missionary school on the Ivory Coast, running a conference for missionary kids. Shortly after we arrived, we heard gunfire in the distance and soon learned that a political coup was under way. As the days went by, the fighting came nearer and nearer until it was right outside our compound.

Suddenly we heard gunfire right next to the front wall of the school campus. Loud noises that sounded like fifty caliber machine guns with tracer bullets, along with smaller arms, resounded across the entire missionary school. The tracers came low over the wall, two and a half meters high, and traveled almost in a flat line. The shots seemed to be aimed across the campus and not down at the ground; it was evident that many of the weapons fired were from the backs of vehicles. When the shooting started, we hurriedly rounded up everyone and flew into the main building to the middle floor, landing flat on the ground in record time. We all lay face down, hugging the cement walls for greater protection, in case any bullets should penetrate our building. The fighting raged on, loudly and fiercely. There had been talk of an evacuation since the previous day, but it had not yet been safe to evacuate us.

That was a day I will never forget as long as I live! There was shooting off and on during the night, sometimes quite close. I didn't sleep much at all that night, not because I felt worried or afraid; I simply couldn't turn off my mind. I kept thinking this whole thing was some kind of strange dream. Then I'd see my co-worker, Joyce, sleeping on her mattress right next to me on the floor, and I knew she wasn't a figment of my imagination.

Joyce and I whispered late into the night, after lights went out, about her two previous evacuations from the Congo, one in which she barely escaped with her life! Joyce whispered about how she had learned to live with danger as an ever-present background stress for most of her missionary life. I asked her, that night, how missionaries come to terms with that. She said it ultimately comes down to knowing God's call on your life. When you know that you're in the center of God's will, you learn to accept what life brings, and you don't question or challenge everything going on around you. Wow!

Listening to the shooting during that night, I found myself truly thanking God for the distinct privilege of being able to experience this coup right alongside my colleagues. What better way to understand the stresses missionaries encounter and to help them deal with those stresses than to experience some of them firsthand myself…and even to walk through one with them.

Sometimes the utter breadth and depth of emotions involved in all the many scenarios of events over those few days is almost too much to comprehend. Where does one go with all this? How does one begin to process and integrate all this stuff? I don't know.

-Ruth Ann Graybill, a Mobile Member Care Worker, September 2002

Childhood And Responsibility

I grew up as the "responsible" missionary kid. My only sister had multiple learning disabilities, and today I realize my dad had ADHD and Tourette's Disorder. I suspect Mom had many times of anxiety. I learned early in childhood that I had to look out for myself because my parents were so busy with their missions work and their own problems, they weren't alert when physically and emotionally dangerous situations happened to me. I don't hold this against them; I believe they did the best they could with what they knew. But I always felt responsible for my family's welfare.

When I was in seventh grade, my mother had a hysterectomy and came home to recover. Shortly afterward Dad left for several weeks of traveling to raise funds for the mission. I was left "in charge" of my Mom and sister. Early the next morning Mom didn't look well. Something inside told me to stay home from school, so I sent Joan off and hung around the house to keep an eye on Mom. Suddenly my mom began to hemorrhage. I remember seeing lots of blood and knowing she was too weak to take care of things herself. I knew I had to "fix it." Panicky, I tried to reach the doctor and several friends with no luck. I was crying and praying for help. Finally I reached a friend who was a nurse, and she got in touch with the right medical people to get my Mom back to the hospital.

I think that was the day I began eating everything in sight. I didn't stop until I had gained forty pounds. Food was my comfort. When I became depressed about the way I looked, my self-esteem hit the floor, and I didn't know how to soothe myself any other way.

Today, I realize that kids who grow up having to be overly responsible miss an important part of their childhood. I have talked to several MK's who were physically or sexually abused on the mission field without their parent's knowledge, and didn't talk about it because they didn't think their parents would believe them or respond appropriately. Sometimes parents worry about one child in the family whose needs are obvious, and ignore the one who seems to "have it all together."

I hope missionary parents will be careful to watch out for their kids' safety, and not put them in charge of responsibilities that are inappropriate for their ages.

-Joyce Pelletier, a clinical counselor, wife, and mother of three children.

Civil War And Violence

My husband and I were missionaries in several different locations in Africa between 1967 and 2001. Our missions work included community development, starting a school, literacy, teaching Bible school, and planting churches in remote areas. We've lived through wars and kidnappings. The American Embassy warned "all Americans evacuate!" but we believed, instead, that the Lord wanted us to stay. Three times we had to leave our mission work suddenly, losing everything we had except the things we could carry out with us during the times of evacuation.

In 1990 we were serving in Liberia when a civil war broke out and it became too dangerous to stay. Our children, at the time attending college in the US, had come to visit us for the summer. As the rebel forces came closer we realized it was again necessary to evacuate quickly to the neighboring country. To get to safety, we had to drive to the border and pass through a border patrol, then cross a bridge into Sierra Leone. At the border our entire family, along with three other Americans, were taken hostage by angry officials and told not to cross. Our son was held and interrogated. As the fighting came closer, we tried twice to cross the bridge, but we were told, "We'll fill your car with bullets!" One of our vehicles was taken from us. We felt it was necessary to build a barricade in an empty room to keep ourselves away from the line of fire.

As the rebels approached, there was a lot of shooting and glass flying all around us. The officials fled but it was not safe to come out. We began yelling, "Americans! Missionaries!" A rebel holding an AK47 came over and told us he had been getting ready to wipe out our barricade when he heard us yelling. For eight days we were held by the rebels, who gave us a place to sleep, but wouldn't release us. We kept our daughter hidden in a back room, fearing for her safety. My husband was desperately sick with malaria, but at the instruction of the rebels went across the bridge to try to get our stolen vehicle back. Although he was unsuccessful, a short-term missionary heard of our plight and came across to plead and negotiate with the rebels to get us released. His skillful bargaining finally convinced them to let us go. We walked across the bridge into Sierra Leone with no belongings other than one handbag each, and no passports, thanking God that we were finally free!

Afterward our mission sent us to North Carolina for a debriefing, which was very helpful. God gave us grace that carried us through this time of crisis. We've seen terrible destruction and death from the war. I've had good emotional support from my husband and from the mission. Still, I can never forget the images and fearful memories of being held hostage. I've had periods of anxiety and fear of the unknown.

-Rachel, is a mother of two, widow, and retired missionary from service in Africa

The Reality Of Suicide

We were missionary kids in the Andes Mountains of South America, attending a Christian School while our parents worked in dozens of ministries throughout the region. In high school I became good friends with Sherry, my neighbor, who was a few years older. We used to talk on the way home from school, and sometimes have sleepovers. During those times she confided in me about the problems with her "rebellious" brothers, who were kicked out of school for an action they didn't commit. Since our school was the primary source of education for missionaries at the time, the expulsion of her brothers brought great duress to the family.

Sherry felt depressed for years. I didn't take her seriously when she made statements like "I feel like dying." I didn't know anything about suicide, and I thought Sherry's talk of dying was just a "normal" expression of distress, or maybe teenage drama, but not an actual threat. I tried to be as much of a friend to Sherry as anyone can be at the age of fifteen. I had no knowledge of mental health. Everything in our world was black and white, sinful or righteous, with nothing in between. We didn't trust the adults in our world to listen to us without judging. I didn't have a clue how to help her.

Distraught over family problems, and feeling like a social outcast at the missionary school, Sherry had periods of irrational thinking. She eventually came to believe that her death would be God's will, and that God wanted her to die to bring her brothers closer to him. One day after I had left for the States, Sherry committed suicide. Her suicide shocked the missionary community. I was wracked with guilt for not having listened to her cries for help and realizing too late that her suicide threats were real.

-Gina, an MK in Ecuador in the 1960's

Conclusion

Most sincere thanks to all the missionaries and MKs who sent us their stories and shared the details of their experiences. Many asked not to be identified, because their work continues in countries where individuals live in danger. They do not want anyone to suffer or experience risk because of having told their stories. A few missionaries remain fearful that sharing their writings will cause them to be seen as failures, or as having a lack of faith, instead of having experienced reasonable responses to abnormal events.

The missionaries who contributed their stories and memories seem to share common characteristics. All have experienced one or more of the signs and symptoms in this book that occurred as a result of a traumatic incident on the mission field. Most of the missionaries expressed gratefulness to God that their lives were spared, and several mentioned how the Lord helped them through the time of crisis by allowing them to think clearly and take action. During the shock, fear, or terror of the moment, God's grace helped to carry them through. Several wrote letters to their supporters immediately afterward outlining how God had been with them and used the event as a significant learning experience in their lives. Most searched for meaning from the traumatic event, believing that within the event, God had a purpose.

Although some experienced sorrow and grief immediately, many of the missionaries did not experience anxiety, depression, or other symptoms until several days, weeks, or months had passed. For some, it was a surprise that they were feeling worse than before, especially because the crisis had passed and they were now in a place of safety. They worried about their mental state and wondered if it was okay to admit they were feeling worse. Lack of understanding about the long-term effects of trauma may increase self-doubt, low self-esteem and can be devastating to the spirit, causing the individual to wonder if lack of faith is to blame for the symptoms.

Other missionaries shut down their feelings and protect themselves with the armor of PTSD so they can continue working on the mission field. Some do not recognize the emotional armor until many years later, although others around them may see their inability to connect emotionally.

Some of these missionaries received support, debriefing, and counseling provided by their home mission, and mentioned that it was helpful. Others received no counseling services, with mixed results. Several mentioned that time had healed the majority of their symptoms. Some received medication and counseling years later, experienced healing, and felt much better as a result. Many had lingering symptoms of anxiety and depression, and were learning how to cope with these symptoms in everyday life.

The writings of missionaries' kids tend to indicate serious, negative effects from trauma. This is in part due to their youth along with the inability to control their circumstances, and the lack of protection they felt during the time of crisis. The serious effects of trauma in childhood can last a lifetime. Most of the MKs were unable to safely discuss their feelings of fear, pain, or terror at the time of crisis for a variety of reasons. Some of them held their secrets for years before they were able to talk openly about physical, sexual, or spiritual abuse. It is our hope and prayer that missionaries will safeguard the innocence of their children and be especially careful to provide care and counseling services for them after traumatic incidents occur.

Appendix 5:
Talking To Kids About
Post-traumatic Stress Disorder
PTSD And Your Loved One:
A Story For Children

If your Mom or Dad
Or Brother or Sister
Or Aunt or Uncle
Or Miss or Mister
Went to the mission field
Or if you are reading this story
You might be living with somebody who has PTSD.
This little story is about a person we call a missionary who has
PTSD.

PTSD stands for Post-Traumatic Stress Disorder.

Post means the missionary you know started to feel really bad After something awful happened.

Traumatic means very, very upsetting. Traumatic things can give you bad dreams and even make your tummy sick.

Stress makes your heart beat faster! Sometimes it gives you a headache.

Disorder means something is wrong, out of order. Living with PTSD can be very hard

Hard for the person who has it
And hard for family and friends like you!

PTSD can make a person really GRUMPY when you think they should be nice.

Sometimes that person might just want to be left alone.
You won't understand—neither will they—maybe.

You won't understand why someone is grumpy and they might not understand either.
It can take a long time to get better from PTSD…
It can take a long time to learn to relax after coming home…

The best thing for *you* to know is that the person you know can get better.
It will take time, love, and understanding.
Have faith—
You are not alone.

PTSD is NOT your fault.
Talk to an adult you trust.
Ask questions until you get answers.
You matter.

Your missionary might be a hero!
Believe that slowly things will get better and better.

Rainbows are painted one color at a time…
***
I'm Jeannie, a missionary kid and I am 10 years old.

Why isn't my daddy like other daddies? Today I don't know if he will be happy or mad.

I like the days when he is happy, because he helps build things for me. We make a cage for my parrot, Tomas. One day I helped Daddy make posts and a crossbar so my friends and I can practice high jumping. Daddy is really fun when he's in a good mood.

Some days my daddy is really awful. He yells for no reason. Sometimes he yells really loud and spanks me with a stick and then tells me I deserve it. He fights with Mom, too. Then he goes to work at the mission station and pretends to be nice to everyone.

Some days I hide in my tree house. I have to make sure my sister and I are safe and that everything is "Okay"…but really, nothing is okay. I have a lot of worries while hiding in my tree house.

I keep busy. Some days I walk on the top of the walls and watch the cows that belong to the Indian lady as they come through the gate.

I want to live next door at my friend's house. Her Mom and Dad are always nice to me. When things are bad at my house, I run over there and pretend that's where I live. I wonder if I should talk to them…but I don't. I am loyal to my missionary parents and keep my feelings inside.

I don't know what will happen next. I smile when I am supposed to smile. I need to tell someone but I don't know who to tell. There must be someone I can trust, but I don't know who that is because I am still small.

Maybe there is a neighbor, teacher, counselor or friend who I can trust. I know there is someone who will help me to feel safe. Does God love me no matter what? Sometimes it doesn't feel like it when Mom and Daddy are fighting and the world is upside down.

I need a safe place when things feel crazy. I need a safe place where I can be me. I need to be able to be honest about what's going on at home and not pretend.
It's really hard trying to be good all the time.
I hope someday I can tell somebody…

Appendix 6:
Choosing A Mental
Health Professional

Missions' organizations often supply counseling services for missionaries within their networks, and provide the first number to call should a crisis arise. Request confidentiality to insure your personal information remains private.

Be aware that counseling professionals are trained at many different levels, and will provide their services accordingly. Ask about the personnel of the organization so you understand the credentials of the person you will be seeing.

Christian psychiatrists, psychologists, and counselors combine their training in mental health with their knowledge of scripture to provide the best services they can offer.

Psychiatrists are PhDs in medicine, physicians who specialize in the diagnoses, prevention, and treatment of mental illnesses, including substance abuse. Psychiatrists are experts in the study of illnesses of the brain, and can prescribe medications to treat a host of mental health illnesses.

Psychologists are PhDs in psychology trained in the study of the human mind. They investigate the physical, cognitive, emotional, or social aspects of human development and behavior. Psychologists, like psychiatrists, may administer psychological testing and assessments, but usually cannot prescribe medication.

Licensed Clinical Social Workers are trained in psychotherapy and help individuals deal with a variety of mental health and daily living problems to improve overall functioning. A social worker usually has a master's degree in social work and has studied sociology, growth and development, mental health theory and practice, human behavior/social environment, psychology, or research methods.

Marriage and Family Therapists are relationship specialists who treat persons involved in interpersonal relationships. They are trained to assess, diagnose and treat individuals, couples, families and groups to achieve more adequate, satisfying and productive marriage, family and social adjustment.

Clinical Counselors and Mental Health Counselors are skilled professionals who are usually educated at a master's level or above, and provide services such as assessment and diagnosis, psychotherapy, treatment planning, therapy, and interventions for mental health issues.

Pastoral Counselors are trained in both psychology and theology as part of their licensure and thus can provide psychological as well as spiritual guidance to patients and families in health care settings.

Marriage and Family Therapists, Social Workers, Clinical Counselors, and Pastoral Counselors may be educated at a master's level or a doctoral level. Their education and training varies according to their place of licensure. They all assess mental health problems and provide appropriate therapies and interventions to assist missionaries who need help.

Nurse Practitioners are post-masters or doctoral-prepared individuals who may provide case management, prescribe medication and offer a variety of individual and group psychotherapy services, sometimes working with physicians and sometimes working on their own as licensed independent providers.

Biblical Counselors may or may not be trained in mental health counseling, depending on their college of training. They use the principles of scripture to assist their clients.

Questions to ask:

1. What is your license? What type of training do you have in mental health? In the study of scripture?
2. How many years experience do you have in your field? In helping missionaries?
3. Have you had experience helping people with (name your problem)?
4. Will all my information remain confidential?
5. Are you required to report back to anyone in my mission? Under what circumstances? If so, will I see the report?
6. What does your care involve, in terms of cost, length, frequency, etc? Do you take insurance?
7. What type of treatment will you provide? What is the expected outcome?

Appendix 7:
Resources For Missionaries

Although we believe the resources listed on the following pages are reputable, we cannot personally endorse any of these programs. We recommend you check the education and references of any caregiver you enlist for services, and ask the questions from Appendix 6.

Alongside, Inc.
A nonprofit organization whose mission is to restore hope, purpose, and relationships among Christian leaders. Individual counseling and family services are available. www.alongsidecares.net

Anderson, Paul, Ph.D.
Christian psychologist
6524 West 106th Street
Overland Park, KS 66212
913-901-9110
www.netpsychologist.com
www.bulletproofcoach.com

Archipelago Resource & Renewal Center
Bali, Indonesia
info@thearrc.org

The Asia Education Resource Consortium (AERC)
Providing important support and targeted services through a network of regional conferences, family consultations, testing services, resource centers, and online resources. www.asiaerc.org/aercj/index.php

Asian Cross-Cultural Training Institute (ACTI)
Providing strategic information and hands-on workshops, interpersonal
relationships, stress management, raising and keeping a missionary family
together, and practicing true discipleship.
www.acti-singapore.org

Barnabus Christian Counseling Network
Providing encouragement and pastoral care to God's global servants,
MKs, and missionaries.
www.barnabus.org

Barnabus Pacific New Zealand
Ministering to those who minister
Barnabus Pacific, Tauranga 3110, New Zealand
www.barnabuspacific.4t.com

Barnabus Zentrum
Baden, Austria
Carl and JoLynn Krause
carljokrause1@juno.com
www.bzentrum.eomweb.org

Brennan, Dr. Robin, Ph.D., MFT
Christian psychologist
P.O. Box 53882
Irvine, CA 92619-3882
714-517-7661
drbrennan@juno.com

Budapest Care Center
Offering mental health services to Christian workers living in Europe,
Russia and Central Asia.
budapestcare.com/default.aspx

Caring for Others, USA
Caring for the relational, emotional, and spiritual needs of Christian
workers.
www.caringforothers.org

Casurella, Mandy, M.A., LPC
Madagascar, Africa
mandycasurella@gmail.com
www.besidethebaobab.com

Center for Counseling and Growth
Dr. Steve Spinella
Da Yi Street, Lane 29, #26, 2F-1, Taichung 40454, TAIWAN
011.886.4.2236.1901
fx 4.2236.2109
cell 9.2894.0514
www.team.org.tw/ccg
spinella@alumni.rice.edu

Christian Counseling Associates
Ken Williams, M.A., LCPC
Stevens Forest Professional Center
9650 Santiago Road, Suite 101
Columbia, MD 21045
410-995-5587
301-596-5759
www.christiancounselingassociates.org
KenW@ChristianCounselingAssociates.org

Christian Counseling Center
Providing affordable counseling, consultation and educational services
through professionals committed to Christ.
1870 Leonard
Grand Rapids, MI 49505
616-956-1122
www.cccwmich.org

Cornerstone Clinic
1825 Academy Drive
Anchorage, AK 99507
907-522-7080
www.cornerstoneclinic.org

Cornerstone Counseling Foundation
285/86 Moo 4 T.Thasala, Muang, Chiang Mai 50000 Thailand
www.cornerstonecounseling.in.th
pamd@cornerstonecounseling.in.th

Dvorak, Mrs. Lois, RNC, LCPC
Clinical Counselor and MK
6 State Street
Bangor, ME 04401
207-947-2292
dvorak22@juno.com

Dzembo, Daniel, LCSW
Social worker and former missionary
Karner Psychological Associates
2280 Western Avenue
Guilderland, NY 12084
ddsundal@nycap.rr.com

Global Member Care Resources, Memca
Resources for the nurture and development of mission aid personnel.
www.globalmembercare.org
For radio services: www.membercareradio.com

Godspeed Services International
Clinical assessments on the field and in the US, counseling, and medical care
4 Dickens Crest
Columbia, SC 29229
www.missionarycare.org

Graybill, Mrs. Ruth Ann
Biola Counseling Center
12625 La Mirada Boulevard, Suite 202
La Mirada, CA 90638
Voice Mail: 562-903-4799, x5403#
Phone: 562-903-4800
Ruth.ann.graybill@biola.edu

Greater Europe Mission Member Care
Norman Tober, M.Div., M.A.
Konigsfeld, Germany
ntober@gemission.com

Headington Institute
Online resources providing training, counseling, and consulting
200 East Del Mar Boulevard, #119
Pasadena, CA 91005
www.headington-institute.org

Heartstream Resources
Providing services of restoration and renewal for cross-cultural workers
101 Herman Lee Circle
Liverpool, PA 17045
717-444-2374
www.heartstreamresources.org

Interaction International
An organization working to meet the needs of Third Culture Kids.
www.interactionintl.org

International Health Management
4000 Leslie Street
North York, ON M2K2R9, Canada
416-494-7512
416-492-3740
www.ihmcanda.org
Duncan P. Westwood, Ph.D.
Clinical Director of Expatriate Care and Development
416-446-0762
admin@ihmcanada.org

International Network for Christian Counseling
Provides information to access Christian counselors across the globe.
www.internationalchristiancounseling.com

Johnson, Cherilyn, M.A., LLPC
Sparrow's Nest Christian Counseling

Farmington, Michigan, former missionary
248-225-0354
ionthesparrow@gmail.com

Koteskey, Ron and Bonnie
Member Care Consultants, New Hope International Ministries
Websites and databases with information to help missionaries
www.missionarycare.com
www.crossculturalworkers.com
email: ron@missionarycare.com

Kreps, Tova LCSW
CTS Wellspring Counseling, Inc
14401 OLD Cuter Road
Miami, FL 33151
305-573-7009

Lanham Laite, Stephanie, PMH-NP, BC
Solomon PTSD Recovery Project
Box 872
Camden, ME 04843
www.solomonrecoveryproject.org
info@solomonrecoveryproject.org
stlrnc@aol.com

Leenhouts, Gerri, LCSW
Psychotherapist, Individual, Marriage-Family, Crisis, Trauma
4235 Kamala Lane
Brookfield, WI 53045
414-588-7051
GLEENHOUTS@wi.rr.com

Les Uns Les Autres, France
Au Service du Corps Pastoral et Missionnaire
Conseil, Consultation, Ressourcement, et Formation
Pour tout renseignement,nhsitez pas nous contacter.
oneanother.com

Life Impact, Oregon USA
Strengthening international workers and Christian leaders.
www.lifeimpactministries.net

Link Care Center
Restoration/Personal Growth, training and consultation, counseling, and crisis debriefing services.
www.linkcare.org

Mandalupe, Lou N, M.A.
Counseling services, Quezon City, Philippines
632 4337222
639 228840593
lou_mandalupe@yahoo.com

Ministry Resources Connection
Providing services for missionaries and their families
7520 Monticello Road
Columbia SC 29211
803-254-3313
www.mresourcesconnection.org

Minnesota Renewal Center
3499 Lexington Avenue North, Suite 100
St. Paul, MN 55126-7055
651-486-4828
mail@minnesotarenewal.org

Mission Training International
Debriefing and renewal services
P.O. Box 1220
Palmer Lake, CO 80133
800-896-3710
www.mti.org

Missionary Care Services
Elizabeth Walker, RN, M.A., LPC
11 W. Davies Avenue
Littleton, CO 80120

www.southwestcounseling.org
sca@sac-solutions.org

Mobile Member Care Team
Training, consultation, counseling, and crisis response
P.O. Box OS-3063
Osu-Accra, Ghana, West Africa
233-21-77-48-82
233-244-77-93-36
233-244-76-12-63
www.mmct.org

Narramore Christian Foundation
A Christian mental health organization dedicated to preventing and
solving human problems, anxiety, depression, relational conflicts, and
psychological disorders through psychological counseling.
www.ncfliving.org

One Another Ministry International, USA
Provides professional counseling, consulting, training and resourcing for
the development and care of mission organizations and their members,
churches on the mission field and their leaders.
www.oneanother.com

Palmer Fry Counseling and Mediation Services
49 Hanover Gardens
London SE115TN
020-78203531
007-74636848

Paraclete Mission Group, Inc
Member care and counseling services
70 South Val Vista Drive, Suite A3, Box 623
Gilbert, AZ 85296
480-854-4444
www.paraclete.net

Pelletier, Mrs. Joyce, M.Ed., LCPC
Clinical Counselor, former MK

1321 Washington Avenue
Portland, ME 04103
207-797-5911
www.joycepelletier.com
www.sunriseseminars.com

Quiet Streams Counseling
Individual, marital, and family counseling
931 E. 86th Street, Suite 101
Indianapolis, IN 46240
317-254-8888
lois@quietstreamscounseling.com

Reinicke Counseling Associates
Aaron J. Reinicke, MFT
233 Camino del Rio South
San Diego, CA
www.RCAcounseling.com

Retreat for Cross-Cultural Workers, Switzerland
Breathe is a 10-day retreat created for the renewal and encouragement
of singles, couples, and families who serve in cross-cultural settings.
Counseling, medical consultation, educational advice, computer tech
support, and massage. Teaching, worship, activities and programs for
children. www.breatheconference.org

Sandoz, Josh, M.A.
Interaction International, Director of ATCK Services
206-283-0963
joshsandoz@interactionintl.org
www.interactionintl.org

Shepherd's Heart Ministry
Shepherd's Sanctuary Retreat Center
South River, Ontario P0A1X0
www.shepherdsheartministry.com

Smith, Timothy J, NBCC, LPC
Vienna, Austria

VoIP: 303-731-5573
james.timothy.smith@gmail.com

Spiritual Growth Ministries New Zealand
Spiritual Growth Ministries for missionaries.
www.sgm.org.nz

Spooner, Mrs. Ursula, M.S.
Pro-Family Counseling Services
Julius-Payergasse 14, 1220 Vienna
0699-1956-4238
profamilycounseling.org
profamilyaustria@yahoo.com

Step Aside For Encouragement (SAFE), Singapore
Step Aside For Encouragement (SAFE) is designed to help give cross-cultural workers a time-out from their busy schedules in order to relax, examine their situation, and plan for the future.
www.acti-singapore.org
admin@acti-singapore.org

Sunrise Seminars
A consortium of counseling professionals who provide training on parenting, relationships, personal growth, and topics of faith
Contact seminar leaders and clinical counselors through the website.
www.sunriseseminars.com

Teal, Allen and Charlotte
Member care services to missionaries, churches, and mission agencies in New Zealand
www.missionarycare.org.nz
teals1@xtra.co.nz

Teik-Cheok Loy, Johnben MBA, MTS
Ph.D. candidate, Marriage & Family Therapy
Location: Kuala Lumpur, Malaysia (starting January 2010)
jloy@umn.edu

Tumaini Counseling Centre
Counseling, psychiatric, and pastoral care services
Nairobi, Kenya
254-20-890039
254-733-687050
www.tumainicounseling.net

Walker, Ben, M.S., L.P.C.
Adventures in Missions Missionary Care Counselor
Sunset International Bible Institute
Providing counseling & missionary care services in person as well as via
phone, email, or video call 3723 34th Street
Lubbock, TX 79410
806-788-3264
bwwalker@sibi.cc

The Well Member Care Center
No.550 Chaing Mai Lampang Super Highway
Tambon Ta Salam Maper Muang, Chang Mai 50000
053-246-801
www.thewellcm.org

Wellspring Counseling Center
700 Old Roswell Lakes Parkway, Suite 250
Roswell, Georgia 30076
770-587-4736
TomQuery@Gmail.com

Westerman, Karen, Ph.D.
Christian Psychologist and former missionary
P.O. 707
Poland Spring, ME 04274
207-998-5172
bunyoni@gmail.com

References

Amen, Daniel G. (1998). *Change your brain, change your life.* New York, NY: Three Rivers Press.

American Psychiatric Association (2000). *Diagnostic and statistical manual of mental disorders.* (4th Ed.) Washington, D.C., American Psychiatric Association.

Bourne, E. (2002). *The anxiety and phobia workbook.* Oakland, CA: New Harbinger Publications.

Erickson, D., Wolfe, J., King, L., & Sharkansky, E. (2001). Posttraumatic stress disorder and depression symptomatology in a sample of gulf war veterans: A prospective analysis. *Journal of Consulting and Clinical Psychology,* 69(1):41-49.

Fawcett, J. (2003). *Stress and trauma handbook.* Monrovia, CA: World Vision International.

Headington Institute, *Spiritual symptoms of trauma.* www.eadingtoninstitute.org/online training.

Herman, J. (2002). *Trauma and recovery.* New York, NY: Basic Books.

International Critical Incident Stress Foundation. *Crisis intervention and critical incident stress management: A defense of the field.* www.icisf.oug/articles.

Jenkins, S., & Baird, B. (2002). Secondary traumatic stress and vicarious trauma: A validational study. *Journal of Traumatic Stress,* 15(5):423-432.

Kaplin, H. & Sadock, B. (1998). *Synopsis of psychiatry: Behavioral sciences/clinical psychiatry.* (8th Ed.). Baltimore, MD: Lippincott Williams & Wilkins.

Koenig, L. (1994). *The making of a happy family.* Baton Rouge, LA: Smart Family Press.

Lewis, C. S. (1962). *The problem of pain.* New York, NY: Macmillan Publishing Company.

Schiraldi, G. R. (2000). *The post-traumatic stress disorder sourcebook: A guide to healing, recovery and growth.* Los Angeles, CA: Lowell House.

Scurfield, R. (2006). *War trauma: Lessons unlearned from Vietnam to Iraq.* (Volume 3 of a Vietnam Trilogy). New York, NY: Algora Publishing.

Stahl, Stephen M. (2007). *Essential psychopharmacology: The prescriber's guide.* New York, NY: Cambridge University Press.

The Quest Study Bible, New International Version (NIV). (1994).Grand Rapids, Michigan: Zondervan Publishing House.

Walser, Robyn D. (2008) *Posttraumatic stress disorder: Aftermath of trauma and terrorism.* National Center for PTSD, Lecture Series: University of Southern Maine.

Yehuda, R. (2002). Current status of cortisol findings in post-traumatic stress disorder. *Psychiatric Clinics of North America,* 25:341-368.

Young, E., & Breslau, N. (2004). Cortisol and catecholamines in posttraumatic stress disorder. Archives of General Psychiatry, 61(4):394-401.